JANE
EYRE

JANE EYRE

a condensation of the book by

CHARLOTTE BRONTË

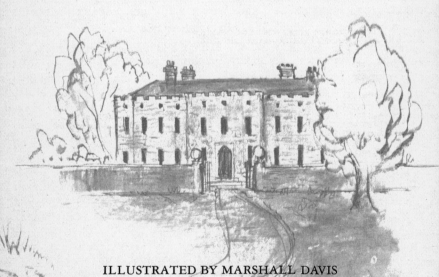

ILLUSTRATED BY MARSHALL DAVIS

The condensation in this volume has been created
by The Reader's Digest Association, Inc.

Copyright © 1987 by The Reader's Digest Association, Inc.
Copyright © 1987 by The Reader's Digest Association (Canada) Ltd.
Copyright © 1987 by Reader's Digest Services Pty. Ltd., Sydney, Australia
Copyright © 1987 by The Reader's Digest Association South Africa (Pty.) Limited
Copyright © 1987 by Reader's Digest Association Far East Limited
Philippines copyright 1987 by Reader's Digest Association Far East Limited
Reader's Digest, The Digest and the Pegasus logo are registered
trademarks of The Reader's Digest Association, Inc. All rights reserved.
Unauthorized reproduction, in any manner, is prohibited.

First Edition

Library of Congress Cataloging-in-Publication Data
Reader's digest
Reader's digest best loved classics.
Pbk. ed. of: Reader's digest best loved books for
young readers. 1st ed. c1966–c1969.
Issued in a case.
Contents: [1.] Little women/by Louisa May Alcott—
[2.] Red Badge of courage/by Stephen Crane—[3.]
Hunchback of Notre Dame/byVictor Hugo—[etc.]
1. Children's literature. [1. Literature—
Collections] I. Reader's digest. II. Title: Best
loved classics. III. Title: Reader's digest best loved
books for young readers.
PZ5.R19857   1987   [Fic]   87-20791
ISBN 0-89577-288-4 (pbk.: set)
ISBN 0-89577-287-6

Printed in the United States of America

In 1847 a London publisher received a manuscript by an unknown writer who signed himself "Currer Bell." It told an original and compelling story about a young woman alone in the world to whom wonderful and tragic things happened, and when *Jane Eyre* was published it became the sensation of the season, eclipsing even *Vanity Fair*, then being published in installments.

But who was this Currer Bell? Not even the publisher knew—until one day a small, quietly dressed woman called on him to announce that *she* was the author of *Jane Eyre*.

Charlotte Brontë was then thirty-one. She came from Haworth, a stone-gray village on the wild Yorkshire moors where the Reverend Patrick Brontë had brought up his six motherless children. With only themselves for companions, the children grew up exploring the moors and filling tiny notebooks with stories of imaginary lands and their people.

Much of *Jane Eyre* is autobiographical. Thus, the Brontë girls were sent to a grim boarding school for the daughters of clergymen; this school became the "Lowood" of the novel. And like her heroine, Charlotte held positions as governess.

For a while she taught in Brussels; but somehow the bleak parsonage at Haworth drew her irresistibly back. There, the narrow life she lived with her sisters Emily and Anne must seem dull and unrewarding. But underneath the surface these three were living an intense life of the imagination charged with genius. For while Charlotte poured out her pent-up emotions in *Jane Eyre*, Anne was writing *Agnes Grey*, and Emily, working usually at night, was creating *Wuthering Heights*.

Before long, however, both Emily and Anne died, and Charlotte was left alone. Then, in her thirty-ninth year, she married a clergyman. It was the first unalloyed happiness of her life; and it lasted just nine months before she, too, died. But as her legacy she left this powerful and moving novel, which Carl Van Doren has called "A truly universal story of love in suffering and triumph."

CHAPTER I

THERE WAS NO POSSIBILITY of taking a walk that day. We had been wandering, indeed, in the leafless shrubbery an hour in the morning; but since dinner (Mrs. Reed, when there was no company, dined early) the cold winter wind had brought with it clouds so somber, and a rain so penetrating, that further outdoor exercise was now out of the question.

I was glad of it. I never liked long walks, especially on chilly afternoons: dreadful to me was the coming home in the raw twilight, with nipped fingers and toes, and a heart saddened by the chidings of Bessie, the nurse, and humbled by the consciousness of my physical inferiority to Eliza, John and Georgiana Reed.

Eliza, John and Georgiana were now clustered round their mama in the drawing room; she lay on a sofa by the fireside, and with her darlings about her (for the time neither quarreling nor crying) looked perfectly happy. Me, she had dispensed from joining the group, saying that she regretted to be under the necessity of keeping me at a distance, but that until she heard from Bessie that I was endeavoring in good earnest to acquire a more sociable and childlike disposition, a more attractive and sprightly manner, she really must exclude me from privileges intended only for contented, happy little children.

"What does Bessie say I have done?" I asked.

"Jane, I don't like questioners. Be seated somewhere; and until you can speak pleasantly, remain silent."

A small breakfast room adjoined the drawing room. I slipped in there. It contained a bookcase: I soon possessed myself of a volume, taking care that it should be one stored with pictures. I mounted into the window seat; gathering up my feet, I sat cross-legged, like a Turk; and, having drawn the red moreen curtain nearly close, I was shrined in double retirement; for the folds of drapery shut in my view to the right, while to the left were the panes of glass separating me from the drear November day.

My book was Bewick's *History of British Birds:* the letterpress thereof I cared little for, generally speaking; but each picture told a story, as interesting as the tales Bessie sometimes narrated on winter evenings when she chanced to be in good humor. With Bewick on my knee, I was then happy: happy at least in my way. I feared nothing but interruption, and that came too soon. The breakfast-room door opened.

"Boh! Madame Mope!" cried the voice of John Reed; then he paused: he found the room apparently empty. "Where the dickens is she?" he continued. "Lizzy! Georgy! Jane is not here. Tell Mama she is run out into the rain—bad animal!"

I wished fervently he might not discover my hiding place; but Eliza put her head in at the door, and said at once: "She is in the window seat, to be sure, Jack."

And I came out immediately, for I trembled at the idea of being dragged forth. "What do you want?" I asked, with awkward diffidence.

"Say, 'What do you want, Master Reed,'" was the answer. "I want you to come here"; and seating himself in an armchair, he intimated by a gesture that I was to stand before him.

John Reed was fourteen years old, four years older than I; large and stout for his age, with a dingy and unwholesome skin. He had not much affection for his mother and sisters, and an antipathy to me. He bullied and punished me continually; every nerve I had feared him. I had no appeal against his inflictions; the servants did not like to offend their young master by taking my

part against him, and Mrs. Reed was blind and deaf on the subject.

Habitually obedient to John, I came up to his chair. He thrust out his tongue at me; then all at once, without speaking, he struck me. I tottered, and retired back a step or two.

"That is for your impudence in answering Mama awhile since," said he, "and for your sneaking way of getting behind curtains. What were you doing behind there?"

"I was reading."

"Show the book."

I returned to the window and fetched it thence.

"You have no business to take our books; you are a dependent, Mama says; your father left you no money; you ought to beg, and not to live here with gentlemen's children like us. Now, I'll teach you to rummage our bookshelves. Go and stand by the door."

I did so, not aware what was his intention; but when I saw him lift and poise the book, I started aside with a cry of alarm. Not soon enough, however; the volume was flung, it hit me and I fell, striking my head against the door and cutting it. The cut bled, the pain was sharp; my terror had passed its climax; other feelings succeeded.

"Wicked and cruel boy!" I said. "You are like a murderer—you are like a slave driver—you are like the Roman emperors!"

"What! What!" he cried. "Did you hear her, Eliza and Georgiana? Won't I tell Mama? But first—"

He ran headlong at me. I felt him grasp my hair and my shoulder. I felt a drop or two of blood trickle down my neck, and was sensible of pungent sufferings: these sensations for the time predominated over fear, and I received him in frantic sort. I don't very well know what I did with my hands, but he called me "Rat! Rat!" and bellowed out aloud. Eliza and Georgiana had run for Mrs. Reed; she now came upon the scene, followed by Bessie and her maid Abbot. We were parted. I heard the words:

"Dear, dear! What a fury to fly at Master John!"

"Did ever anybody see such a picture of passion!"

Then Mrs. Reed subjoined, "Take her away to the red room, and lock her in there."

Four hands were laid upon me, and I was borne upstairs. I resisted all the way, a new thing for me. The fact is, I was a trifle beside myself; I was conscious that a moment's mutiny had already rendered me liable to strange penalties, and, like any other rebel slave, I felt resolved, in my desperation, to go all lengths.

"Hold her arms, Miss Abbot: she's like a mad cat."

"For shame!" cried the lady's maid. "What shocking conduct, Miss Eyre, to strike a young gentleman, your young master!"

"Master! How is he my master? Am I a servant?"

"No; you are less than a servant, for you do nothing for your keep. There, sit down, and think over your wickedness."

They had got me by this time into the apartment indicated by Mrs. Reed, and had thrust me upon a stool. My impulse was to rise from it like a spring; their two pair of hands arrested me instantly.

"If you don't sit still, you must be tied down," said Bessie. "Miss Abbot, lend me your garters; she would break mine directly."

Miss Abbot turned to divest a stout leg of the necessary ligature. This preparation for bonds took a little of the excitement out of me.

"Don't," I cried; "I will not stir." In guarantee whereof, I attached myself to my seat by my hands.

"Mind you don't," said Bessie; and when she had ascertained that I was really subsiding, she loosened her hold of me; then she and Miss Abbot stood with folded arms, looking doubtfully on my face.

"She never did so before," at last said Bessie.

"But it was always in her," was the reply. "I've told Missis often my opinion about the child; she's an under'and little thing."

Bessie answered not; but ere long, addressing me, she said, "You ought to be aware, Miss, that you are under obligations to Mrs. Reed; if she were to turn you off, you would have to go to the poorhouse."

I had nothing to say to these words; they were not new to me.

"What we tell you is for your good," added Bessie, in no harsh voice. "You should try to be useful and pleasant, then, perhaps, you would have a home here; but if you become passionate and rude, Missis will send you away, I am sure."

They went, shutting the door, and locking it behind them.

The red room was a spare chamber, very seldom slept in; yet it was one of the largest and stateliest in Gateshead Hall. A massive mahogany bed, hung with curtains of deep red damask, stood out in the center; the two large windows, with their blinds always drawn down, were half shrouded in festoons of similar drapery; the carpet was red; the table at the foot of the bed was covered with a crimson cloth. Out of these deep surrounding shades rose high, and glared white, the piled-up mattresses and pillows of the bed.

This room was chill, because it seldom had a fire; it was silent, because remote from the nursery and kitchens; solemn, because it was known to be so seldom entered. Mrs. Reed herself, at far intervals, visited it to review the contents of a certain drawer in the wardrobe, where were stored divers parchments and a miniature of her deceased husband; and in those last words lies the secret of the bedroom. Mr. Reed had been dead nine years. In this chamber he breathed his last; here he lay in state; hence his coffin was borne by the undertaker's men; and, since that day, a sense of dreary consecration had guarded it from frequent intrusion.

My seat, to which Bessie and Miss Abbot had left me riveted, was a low ottoman near the marble chimneypiece; to my right hand there was a high, dark wardrobe; to my left were the muffled windows; a great looking glass between them repeated the vacant majesty of the bed and room. I was not quite sure whether they had locked the door; and, when I dared move, I got up and went to see. Alas, yes! No jail was ever more secure. Returning, I had to cross before the looking glass; my fascinated glance involuntarily explored the depth it revealed. All looked colder and darker in that visionary hollow than in reality; and the strange little figure there gazing at me, with a white face and arms specking the gloom, and glittering eyes of fear moving where all else was still, had the effect of a real spirit. I thought it like one of the tiny phantoms, half fairy, half imp, Bessie's evening stories represented as coming up out of lone, ferny dells in moors, and appearing before the eyes of belated travelers.

I returned to my stool. Superstition was with me at that moment, but it was not yet her hour for complete victory: my blood was still warm; the mood of the revolted slave was still bracing me with its bitter vigor. All John Reed's violent tyrannies, all his mother's aversion, all the servants' partiality, turned up in my disturbed mind. Why was I always browbeaten, forever condemned? Why could I never please? Eliza, who was headstrong and selfish, was respected. Georgiana, who had a spoiled temper, was universally indulged. Her beauty, her pink cheeks and golden curls seemed to give delight to all who looked at her. John, no one thwarted, much less punished; though he twisted the necks of the pigeons, set the dogs at the sheep, and stripped the hothouse vines of their fruit. I strove to fulfill every duty, and I was termed naughty and tiresome, sullen and sneaking, from morning to noon, and from noon to night.

Daylight began to forsake the red room; the beclouded afternoon was tending to drear twilight. I heard the rain still beating continuously on the staircase window, and the wind howling; I grew by degrees cold as a stone, and then my courage sank, and my habitual mood of self-doubt returned. All said I was wicked, and perhaps I might be so. Was I fit to die? Was the vault under the chancel of Gateshead Church an inviting bourn? In such vault I had been told did Mr. Reed lie buried; and led by this thought to recall him, I dwelt on the idea of him with gathering dread. I could not remember him; but I knew that he was my own uncle—my mother's brother—that he had taken me when a parentless infant to his house.

I knew that my father had been a poor clergyman; that my mother had married him against the wishes of her father, who had then cut her off without a shilling; that after my mother and father had been married a year, both had caught the typhus fever and had died within a month of each other. I knew also that in my uncle's last moments he had required a promise of Mrs. Reed that she would rear me as one of her own children. Mrs. Reed probably considered she had kept this promise, and so she had, I daresay, as well as her nature would permit her; but it must have been most irksome to find herself bound by a hard-wrung pledge to stand in the stead of a parent to a strange child she could not love.

A singular notion dawned upon me. I doubted not—never doubted—that if Mr. Reed had been alive he would have treated me kindly; and now, as I sat looking at the white bed, the over-shadowed walls and the dimly gleaming mirror, I began to recall what I had heard of dead men, troubled in their graves by the violation of their last wishes, revisiting the earth; and I thought Mr. Reed's spirit might quit its abode and rise before me in this chamber. I hushed my sobs, fearful lest any sign of violent grief might waken a preternatural voice to comfort me, or elicit from the gloom some haloed face, bending over me with strange pity. This idea, consolatory in theory, I felt would be terrible if re-alized. With all my might I endeavored to stifle it. Shaking my hair from my eyes, I lifted my head and tried to look boldly round the dark room. At this moment a light gleamed on the wall; while I gazed, it glided up to the ceiling and quivered over my head. This light was, in all likelihood, a gleam from a lantern, carried by someone across the lawn; but then, prepared as my mind was for horror, shaken as my nerves were by agitation, I thought the swift-darting beam was a herald of some coming vision from an-other world. My heart beat thick, my head grew hot; I was oppressed, suffocated. Endurance broke down; I rushed to the door and shook it in desperate effort. Steps came running along the passage; the key turned, Bessie and Abbot entered.

"Miss Eyre, are you ill?" said Bessie.

"Take me out! Let me go into the nursery!" was my cry.

"What for? Are you hurt? Have you seen something?" again demanded Bessie.

"Oh! I saw a light, and I thought a ghost would come." I had now got hold of Bessie's hand, and she did not snatch it from me.

"She has screamed out on purpose," declared Abbot, in disgust. "If she had been in pain one would have excused it, but she only wanted to bring us here."

"What is all this?" demanded another voice, and Mrs. Reed came along the corridor. "Abbot and Bessie, I believe I gave orders that Jane Eyre should be left in the red room till I came to her myself."

"Miss Jane screamed so loud, ma'am," pleaded Bessie.

"Let her go," was the only answer. "Loose Bessie's hand, child; you cannot succeed in getting out by these means. You will now stay here an hour longer, and only on condition of perfect sub-mission shall I liberate you then."

"Oh, Aunt, have pity! I cannot endure it!"

"Silence! This violence is all most repulsive": and so, no doubt, she felt it. Impatient of my now frantic anguish and wild sobs, she abruptly thrust me back and locked me in, without further parley. I heard her sweeping away; and soon after she was gone I suppose I had a species of fit: unconsciousness closed the scene.

THE NEXT THING I remember is waking up with a feeling as if I had had a frightful nightmare and seeing before me a terrible red glare. In five minutes more, the cloud of bewilderment dis-solved: I knew that I was in my own bed, and that the red glare was the nursery fire. It was night: a candle burned on the table; Bessie stood at the bed-foot and a gentleman sat in a chair near my pillow.

I felt a soothing conviction of protection and security when I knew that there was a stranger in the room, an individual not belonging to Gateshead. Turning from Bessie, I scrutinized the face of the gentleman: it was Mr. Lloyd, an apothecary, sometimes called in by Mrs. Reed when the servants were ailing; for herself and the children she employed a physician.

"Well, who am I?" he asked.

I pronounced his name, offering him at the same time my hand; he took it, smiling and saying, "We shall do very well by and by." Then, addressing Bessie, he charged her to be very careful that I was not disturbed during the night. Having intimated that he should call again the next day, he departed. To my grief—I had felt so sheltered and befriended while he sat near me.

"Do you feel as if you could sleep, miss?" asked Bessie.

"I will try."

"Would you like to drink, or could you eat anything?"

"No, thank you, Bessie."

"Then I think I shall go to bed, for it is past twelve o'clock; but you may call me if you want anything in the night."

Wonderful civility this! It emboldened me to ask a question.

"Bessie, what is the matter with me? Am I ill?"

"You fell sick, I suppose, in the red room with crying; you'll be better soon, no doubt."

For me, the watches of that long night passed in ghastly wakefulness; ear, eye and mind were alike strained by dread, such dread as children only can feel. Next day, however, by noon, I was up and dressed, and sat wrapped in a shawl by the nursery hearth. I felt physically weak, but my worse ailment was an unutterable wretchedness of mind which kept drawing from me silent tears. Yet, I thought, I ought to have been happy, for none of the Reeds were there: they were all gone out in the carriage with their mama; Abbot, too, was sewing in another room, and Bessie, as she moved hither and thither, putting away toys and arranging drawers, addressed to me every now and then a word of unwonted kindness.

In the course of the morning, Mr. Lloyd came again. "What, already up!" said he. "Well, nurse, how is she?"

Bessie answered that I was doing very well.

"Then she ought to look more cheerful. Come here, Miss Jane; your name is Jane, is it not?"

"Yes, sir, Jane Eyre."

"Well, you have been crying, Miss Jane Eyre. Can you tell me what about? Have you any pain?"

"No, sir."

"Oh, I daresay she is crying because she could not go out with Missis in the carriage," interposed Bessie.

My self-esteem being wounded by the false charge, I answered promptly, "I never cried for such a thing in my life: I hate going out in the carriage. I cry because I am miserable."

"Oh fie, Miss!" said Bessie.

The good apothecary appeared a little puzzled. I was standing before him; he fixed his eyes on me, very steadily, and said, "What made you ill yesterday?"

"She had a fall," said Bessie, again putting in her word.

"Fall! Why, that is like a baby! Can't she manage to walk at her age? She must be eight or nine years old."

"I was knocked down," was the blunt explanation jerked out of me by another pang of mortified pride. "But that did not make me ill," I added, while Mr. Lloyd helped himself to a pinch of snuff.

As he was returning the box to his waistcoat pocket, a bell rang for the servants' dinner; he knew what it was. "That's for you, nurse," said he; "you can go down. I'll give Miss Jane a lecture till you come back."

Bessie would rather have stayed, but she went.

"The fall did not make you ill; what did, then?" pursued Mr. Lloyd.

"I was shut up in a room where there is a ghost, till after dark."

Mr. Lloyd smiled. "Ghost! What, you are a baby after all! You are afraid of ghosts?"

"Of Mr. Reed's ghost I am: he died in that room. Neither Bessie nor anyone else will go into it at night; and it was cruel to shut me up alone without a candle. I shall never forget it."

"Nonsense! And is it that makes you so miserable? Are you afraid now in daylight?"

"No; but night will come again before long, and besides— I am very unhappy, for other things."

"What other things? Can you tell me some of them?"

How much I wished to reply fully to this question! How difficult it was to frame any answer! Children can feel, but they cannot analyze their feelings or express them in words. Fearful, however, of losing this opportunity of relieving my grief, I contrived to frame a meager, though, as far as it went, true response.

"For one thing, I have no father or mother, brothers or sisters."

"You have a kind aunt and cousins."

Again I paused; then bunglingly enounced, "But John Reed knocked me down, and my aunt shut me up in the red room."

Mr. Lloyd a second time produced his snuffbox. "Don't you think Gateshead Hall a beautiful house?" asked he. "Are you not thankful to have such a fine place to live at?"

"It is not my house, sir; and Abbot says I have less right to be here than a servant. If I had anywhere else to go, I should be glad to leave it; but I can never get away from Gateshead till I am a woman."

"Perhaps you may—who knows? Have you any relations besides Mrs. Reed?"

"I think not, sir. I asked Aunt Reed once, and she said possibly I might have some poor, low relations called Eyre, belonging to my father, but she knew nothing about them."

"If you had such, would you like to go to them?"

I reflected. Poverty looks grim to grown people, still more so to children. I shook my head.

"Would you like to go to school?"

Again I reflected: I scarcely knew what school was. But school would be a complete change: it implied a journey, a separation from Gateshead, an entrance into a new life.

"I should indeed like to go to school," was my conclusion.

"Well, well; who knows what may happen?" said Mr. Lloyd, as he got up. "The child ought to have change of air and scene," he added, speaking to himself; "nerves not in a good state."

Bessie now returned; at the same moment the carriage was heard rolling up the gravel walk.

"Is that your mistress, nurse?" asked Mr. Lloyd. "I should like to speak to her before I go."

Bessie invited him to walk into the breakfast room, and led the way out.

CHAPTER II

FROM MY DISCOURSE WITH Mr. Lloyd, I gathered enough of hope to wish to get well: a change seemed near. It tarried, however; days and weeks passed; Mrs. Reed surveyed me at times with a severe eye, but seldom addressed me. Since my illness, she had drawn a more marked line of separation than ever between me and her own children, condemning me to take my meals alone and pass all my time in the nursery, while my cousins were constantly in the drawing room.

Eliza and Georgiana, evidently acting according to orders, spoke to me as little as possible; John thrust his tongue in his cheek whenever he saw me, and once attempted chastisement; but as I instantly turned against him, roused by the same sentiment of desperate revolt which had stirred me before, he thought it better to desist, and ran from me vowing I had burst his nose. I heard him in a blubbering tone commence the tale of how "that nasty Jane Eyre" had flown at him like a mad cat. He was stopped rather harshly by his mama:

"Don't talk to me about her, John. I told you not to go near her; I do not choose that either you or your sisters should associate with her."

Here, leaning over the banister, I cried out suddenly, and without at all deliberating:

"They are not fit to associate with me."

Mrs. Reed was a stout woman; but, on hearing this audacious declaration, she ran nimbly up the stair, swept me like a whirlwind into the nursery, and, crushing me down on the edge of my crib, she shook me most soundly, boxed my ears, and then left me without a word.

November, December and half of January passed away. Christmas and the New Year had been celebrated at Gateshead with the usual festive cheer. From every enjoyment I was, of course, excluded; my share of the gaiety consisted in seeing Eliza and Georgiana descend to the drawing room, dressed in muslin frocks and scarlet sashes; and afterwards, in listening to the sound of the piano or the harp played below, to the jingling of china as refreshments were handed, to the broken hum of conversation as the drawing-room doors opened and closed. When tired of this occupation, I would retire from the stair head to the solitary and silent nursery: there, I would sit with my doll on my knee till the fire got low and it was time to undress and get into my crib.

Long did the hours seem while I waited the departure of the company, and listened for the sound of Bessie's step on the stairs; sometimes she would come up to seek her thimble, or perhaps to bring me a bun—then she would sit on the bed while I ate it, and when I had finished, she would tuck the clothes round me, and twice she kissed me, and said, "Good night, Miss Jane." When thus gentle, Bessie seemed to me the best, kindest being in the world; and I wished intensely that she would always be so pleasant and never push me about or scold. Bessie Lee must, I think, have been a girl of good natural capacity; she was pretty, too. I remember her as a slim young woman, with black hair, dark eyes and nice features. She had a capricious and hasty temper; still, I preferred her to anyone else at Gateshead Hall.

It was the fifteenth of January, about nine in the morning. Bessie was gone down to breakfast; my cousins had not yet been summoned to their mama; Eliza was putting on her bonnet and warm coat to go feed her poultry, an occupation of which she was fond; Georgiana sat dressing her hair at the glass, and interweaving her curls with artificial flowers, of which she had found a store in the attic. I was making my bed, having received strict orders from Bessie to get it arranged before she returned. Having spread the quilt, I went to the window seat; for lack of other occupation, I fell to breathing on the frost flowers with which the window was fretted, and thus clearing a space in the glass through which I might look out on the grounds.

From this window was visible the porter's lodge, and as I looked I saw the gates thrown open and a carriage roll through. It stopped in front of the house, the doorbell rang, the newcomer was admitted. All this being nothing to me, my vacant attention soon found livelier attraction in the spectacle of a little hungry robin which came and chirruped on the twigs of a leafless cherry tree near the casement. The remains of my breakfast stood on the table, and, having crumbled a morsel of roll, I was tugging at the sash to put out the crumbs on the sill, when Bessie came running into the nursery.

"Miss Jane, take off your pinafore; have you washed your hands and face this morning? Careless child! What were you opening the window for?"

I was spared the trouble of answering, for Bessie seemed in too great a hurry to listen to explanations; she hauled me to the washstand, inflicted a brief scrub on my face and hands, disciplined my head with a brush, denuded me of my pinafore, and then, hurrying me to the stairs, bid me go down directly as I was wanted in the breakfast room.

I would have asked who wanted me, but Bessie was already gone. I slowly descended, intimidated and trembling. For nearly three months, I had never been called to Mrs. Reed's presence; restricted so long to the nursery, the breakfast, dining and drawing rooms were become for me awful regions, on which it dismayed me to intrude. In agitated hesitation I turned the stiff door handle of the breakfast room. The handle turned, the door unclosed, and passing through and curtsying low, I looked up at—a black pillar! Such, at least, appeared to me at first sight the straight, narrow, sable-clad shape standing erect on the rug.

Mrs. Reed made a signal to me to approach; I did so, and she introduced me to the stranger: "This is the little girl respecting whom I applied to you."

He, for it was a man, turned his head slowly towards where I stood, and having examined me with the two inquisitive-looking gray eyes which twinkled under a pair of bushy brows, said solemnly, and in a bass voice, "Her size is small: what is her age?"

"Ten years."

"So much?" was the doubtful answer. Presently he addressed me: "Your name, little girl?"

"Jane Eyre, sir."

"Well, Jane Eyre, and are you a good child?"

Impossible to reply to this in the affirmative: my little world held a contrary opinion. I was silent. Mrs. Reed answered for me. "Perhaps the less said on that subject the better, Mr. Brocklehurst."

"Sorry indeed to hear it! She and I must have some talk"; and bending from the perpendicular, he installed his person in an armchair. "Come here," he said.

I stepped across the rug; he placed me square and straight before him. What a face he had, now that it was almost on a level with mine! What a great nose! And what large prominent teeth!

"No sight so sad as that of a naughty child," he began. "Do you know where the wicked go after death?"

"They go to hell," was my ready and orthodox answer.

"And what is hell?"

"A pit full of fire."

"And should you like to fall into that pit?"

"No, sir."

"What must you do to avoid it?"

I deliberated a moment; my answer, when it did come, was objectionable: "I must keep in good health, and not die."

"How can you keep in good health? Children younger than you die daily. I buried a little child of five years old only a day or two since—a good little child, whose soul is now in heaven. It is to be feared the same could not be said of you, were you to be called hence."

Not being in a condition to remove his doubts I only cast my eyes down on the two large feet planted on the rug, and sighed, wishing myself far away.

"I hope that sigh is from the heart, and that you repent of ever having been the occasion of discomfort to your benefactress."

At this moment Mrs. Reed interposed, telling me to sit down; she then proceeded to carry on the conversation herself.

"Mr. Brocklehurst, I believe I intimated, in the letter which I wrote to you three weeks ago, that this little girl has not quite the character I could wish. Should you admit her into Lowood school, I should be glad if the superintendent and teachers were requested to keep a strict eye on her, and above all, to guard against her worst fault, a tendency to deceit, a tendency to tell lies. I mention this in your hearing, Jane, that you may not attempt to impose on Mr. Brocklehurst."

Well might I dislike Mrs. Reed! Uttered before a stranger, her accusation cut me to the heart. I dimly perceived that she was already obliterating hope from the new phase of existence which she destined me to enter; I saw myself transformed under Mr. Brocklehurst's eye into an artful, noxious child.

"Deceit is, indeed, a sad fault in a child," said Mr. Brocklehurst. "She shall be watched, Mrs. Reed; I will speak to Miss Temple and the teachers."

"I should wish her to be brought up in a manner suiting her prospects," continued my benefactress; "to be made useful, to be kept humble; as for the vacations, she will, with your permission, spend them at Lowood."

"Your decisions are judicious, madam," returned Mr. Brocklehurst. "Humility is a Christian grace, and one peculiarly appropriate to the pupils of Lowood; I, therefore, direct that especial care be bestowed on its cultivation amongst them."

"This is the state of things I quite approve," returned Mrs. Reed; "had I sought all England over, I could scarcely have found a system more fitting a child like Jane. I will send her then, as soon as possible, Mr. Brocklehurst; for, I assure you, I feel anxious to be relieved of a responsibility that was becoming irksome."

"No doubt, madam, and now I wish you good morning. I shall send Miss Temple notice that she is to expect a new girl, so that there will be no difficulty about receiving her. Good-by."

"Good-by, Mr. Brocklehurst."

Mrs. Reed and I were left alone. Some minutes passed in silence; she was sewing, I was watching her. Mrs. Reed might be at that time some six or seven and thirty; she was a woman of robust frame, with a somewhat large face; her brow was low, her hair flaxen.

Sitting on a low stool, a few yards from her armchair, I examined her figure; I perused her features. What Mrs. Reed had said concerning me to Mr. Brocklehurst, the whole tenor of their conversation, was recent, raw and stinging in my mind. A passion of resentment fomented now within me.

Mrs. Reed looked up from her sewing; her eye settled on mine.

"Go out of the room; return to the nursery," was her mandate. My look must have struck her as offensive, for she spoke with extreme irritation. I got up, I went to the door; I came back again; I walked to the window, across the room, then close up to her.

Speak I must: I had been trodden on severely and *must* turn, but how? I gathered my energies and launched them in this blunt sentence:

"I am not deceitful. If I were, I should say I loved *you;* but I declare I do not love you; I dislike you the worst of anybody in the world except John Reed. As for being a liar, it is your girl Georgiana who tells lies, and not I." Shaking now from head to foot, thrilled with ungovernable excitement, I continued, "I am glad you are no relation of mine. I will never call you aunt again as long as I live; and if anyone ever asks me how you treated me, I will say that you treated me with miserable cruelty."

"How dare you affirm that, Jane Eyre?"

"How dare I, Mrs. Reed? How dare I? Because it is the *truth*. You think I have no feelings, and that I can do without one bit of love or kindness, but I cannot live so; and you have no pity. I shall remember to my dying day how you thrust me back into the red room and locked me up there. And that punishment you made me suffer because your wicked boy knocked me down. I will tell anybody who asks me questions this exact tale. People think you a good woman, but you are bad. *You* are deceitful!"

Ere I had finished this reply, my soul began to expand with the strangest sense of freedom I ever felt. It seemed as if an invisible bond had burst, and that I had struggled out into unhoped-for liberty. Not without cause was this sentiment: Mrs. Reed looked frightened; she was even twisting her face as if she would cry.

"Jane, what is the matter with you? I assure you, I desire to be your friend."

"Not you. You told Mr. Brocklehurst I had a deceitful disposition; and I'll let everybody at Lowood know what you have done."

"Jane, you don't understand these things; children must be corrected for their faults."

"Deceit is not my fault!" I cried out in a savage, high voice.

"But you are passionate, Jane, that you must allow; and now return to the nursery—there's a dear—and lie down a little."

"I am not your dear; I cannot lie down. Send me to school soon, Mrs. Reed, for I hate to live here."

"I will indeed send her to school soon," murmured Mrs. Reed; and gathering up her work, she abruptly quitted the apartment.

I was left there alone—winner of the field. It was the hardest battle I had fought, and the first victory I had gained. I stood awhile on the rug, where Mr. Brocklehurst had stood, and I enjoyed my conqueror's solitude. First, I smiled to myself and felt elated; but this fierce pleasure fast subsided. A child cannot quarrel with its elders, as I had done, without experiencing afterwards the pang of remorse and the chill of reaction. Something of vengeance I had tasted for the first time; as aromatic wine it seemed, on swallowing, warm and racy; but its after-flavor, metallic and corroding, gave me a sensation as if I had been poisoned.

CHAPTER III

FIVE O'CLOCK HAD HARDLY STRUCK on the morning of the nineteenth of January when Bessie brought a candle into my closet and found me already up and dressed. I was to leave Gateshead that day by a coach which passed the lodge gates at six a.m. Bessie was the only person yet risen; she had lit a fire in the nursery, where she now made my breakfast. Few children can eat when excited with the thoughts of a journey; nor could I. Bessie, having pressed me in vain to take a few spoonfuls of boiled milk and bread she had prepared for me, wrapped up some biscuits in a paper and put them into my bag; then she helped me on with my pelisse and bonnet, and she and I left the nursery. As we passed Mrs. Reed's bedroom, she said, "Will you go in and bid Missis good-by?"

"No, Bessie: she came to my crib last night and said I need not disturb her in the morning, or my cousins either; and she told me to remember that she had always been my friend, and to be grateful."

"What did you say, Miss?"

"Nothing. I covered my face with the bedclothes, and turned from her to the wall."

"That was wrong, Miss Jane."

"It was right, Bessie; your Missis has not been my friend."

"Oh, Miss Jane, don't say so!"

26

"Good-by to Gateshead!" cried I, as we passed through the hall and went out at the front door.

It was very dark; Bessie carried a lantern, whose light glanced on wet steps. Raw and chill was the winter morning; my teeth chattered as we hastened down the drive. The distant roll of wheels announced the coming coach.

"Is she going by herself?" asked the porter's wife.

"Yes."

"And how far is it?"

"Fifty miles."

"What a long way! I wonder Mrs. Reed is not afraid to trust her so far alone."

The coach drew up; there it was at the gates with its four horses and its top laden with passengers. My trunk was hoisted up; I was taken from Bessie's neck, to which I clung with kisses.

"Be sure and take good care of her," cried she to the guard, as he lifted me inside.

"Aye, aye!" was the answer; the door was slapped to, and on we drove.

I remember but little of the journey: I only know that it seemed to me we traveled hundreds of miles. The afternoon came on wet and misty; as it waned into dusk, I began to feel that we were getting very far indeed from Gateshead. The country changed; great gray hills heaved up round the horizon; as twilight deepened, we descended a valley, dark with wood, and I heard a wild wind rushing amongst trees. Lulled by the sound, I at last dropped asleep. I had not long slumbered when the sudden cessation of motion awoke me; the coach door was open, and a person like a servant was standing at it.

"Is there a little girl called Jane Eyre here?" she asked. I answered "Yes," and was then lifted out; my trunk was handed down, and the coach instantly drove away.

I was stiff with long sitting, and bewildered with the noise and motion of the coach; gathering my faculties, I looked about me. Rain, wind and darkness filled the air; nevertheless, I dimly discerned a wall before me and a door in it. Through this door I passed with my new guide. There was now visible a house with many windows, and lights burning in some; we went up a path, splashing wet, and were admitted at a door; then the servant led me through a passage into a room with a fire, where she left me.

I stood and warmed my numbed fingers over the blaze, then I looked round; it was a parlor, not so splendid as the drawing room at Gateshead, but comfortable enough. I was puzzling to make out a picture on the wall when the door opened, and two individuals entered. The first was a tall lady with dark hair, dark eyes and a pale and large forehead.

"The child is very young to be sent alone," said she, considering me attentively, then further added, "She had better be put to bed soon. Are you tired?" she asked, placing her hand on my shoulder.

"A little, ma'am."

"And hungry too, no doubt. Let her have some supper before she goes to bed, Miss Miller. Is this the first time you have left your parents to come to school, my little girl?"

I explained to her that I had no parents. She inquired how long they had been dead; then how old I was, whether I could read, write and sew; then she touched my cheek gently, and, saying she hoped I should be a good child, dismissed me along with Miss Miller.

The lady I had left might be about twenty-nine; the one who went with me appeared some years younger. The first impressed me by her voice, look and air. Miss Miller was more ordinary; hurried in gait and action, like one who had a multiplicity of tasks on hand: she looked, indeed, what I afterwards found she was, an under-teacher. Led by her, I passed from compartment to compartment of a large and irregular building till we came upon the hum of many voices, and presently entered a wide, long room, with great deal tables, two at each end, on each of which burned a pair of candles, and seated all round on benches, a congregation of girls of every age, from nine or ten to twenty. Seen by the dim light of the dips, their number to me appeared countless, though not in reality exceeding eighty; they were uniformly dressed in brown stuff frocks of quaint fashion, and long holland pinafores.

It was the hour of study; the hum I had heard was the combined result of their whispered repetitions of tomorrow's task.

Miss Miller signed to me to sit on a bench near the door, then walking up to the top of the long room, she cried out, "Monitors, collect the lesson books and put them away!"

Four tall girls arose from different tables, and going round, gathered the books and removed them. Miss Miller again gave a command, "Monitors, fetch the supper trays!"

The tall girls went out and returned, each bearing a tray, with portions of something arranged thereon, and a pitcher of water and mug in the middle of each tray. The portions were handed round; those who liked took a draft of the water, the mug being common to all. When it came to my turn, I drank, for I was thirsty, but did not touch the food, excitement and fatigue rendering me incapable of eating; I now saw that it was a thin oaten cake, shared into fragments.

The meal over, prayers were read by Miss Miller, and the classes filed off, two and two, upstairs. Overpowered by this time with weariness, I scarcely noticed what sort of place the bedroom was, except that I saw it was very long, with long rows of beds. Tonight I was to be Miss Miller's bedfellow; she helped me to undress. In ten minutes the single light was extinguished; amid silence and complete darkness I fell asleep.

The night passed rapidly: I was too tired even to dream. When I again unclosed my eyes, a loud bell was ringing. The girls were up and dressing; day had not yet begun to dawn, and a rushlight or two burned in the room. I too rose reluctantly; it was bitter cold, and I dressed as well as I could for shivering, in a uniform dress which Miss Miller gave me. Again the bell rang; all the girls formed in file, two and two, descended the stairs and entered the dimly lit schoolroom. Here prayers were read by Miss Miller; afterwards she called out, "Form classes!"

A great tumult succeeded for some minutes, during which Miss Miller repeatedly exclaimed, "Order!" When it subsided, I saw the girls all drawn up in four semicircles, before four chairs placed at the four tables; all held books in their hands, and a great book, like a Bible, lay on each table, before the vacant seat. Three ladies now entered the room, each walked to a table and took her seat; Miss Miller assumed the fourth vacant chair, around which the smallest of the children were assembled; to this class I was called, and placed at the bottom of it.

Business now began: the day's Collect was repeated, and to this succeeded reading of chapters in the Bible. By the time that exercise was terminated, day had fully dawned, and the classes were marched into another room to breakfast. How glad I was to behold a prospect of getting something to eat! I was now nearly sick from inanition, having taken so little the day before. On two long tables smoked basins of something hot, which, however, to my dismay, sent forth an odor far from inviting. From the van of the procession rose the whispered words:

"Disgusting! The porridge is burnt again!"

"Silence!" ejaculated a voice—not that of Miss Miller, but one of the upper teachers, a little and dark personage. A long grace was said; then the meal began. Ravenous, and now faint, I devoured a spoonful or two of my portion; but, the first edge of hunger blunted, I perceived I had got in hand a nauseous mess: burnt porridge is almost as bad as rotten potatoes. The spoons were moved slowly; I saw each girl taste her food and try to swallow, but in most cases the effort was soon relinquished. Thanks being returned for what we had not got, the refectory was evacuated for the schoolroom. I was one of the last to go out, and in passing the tables, I heard one teacher whisper to another:

"Abominable stuff! How shameful!"

A quarter of an hour passed before lessons again began, during which the schoolroom was in a glorious tumult; for that space of time it seemed to be permitted to talk freely. The whole conversation ran on the breakfast, which one and all abused roundly. Then a clock struck nine, and Miss Miller cried, "To your seats!"

Discipline prevailed: in five minutes the confused throng was resolved into order. Ranged on benches down the sides of the room, the eighty girls sat motionless and erect. A quaint assemblage they appeared, all with plain locks combed from their faces, not a curl visible, in their brown uniform dresses, made high and finished with a narrow tucker about the throat.

I was still looking at them when the whole school rose simultaneously, as if moved by a common spring. Ere I had gathered my wits, the classes were again seated, but, as all eyes were now turned to one point, mine followed the general direction and encountered the personage who had received me last night. She stood at the bottom of the long room, on the hearth; she surveyed the two rows of girls silently and gravely, and then said aloud:

"Monitor of the first class, fetch the globes!"

While the direction was being executed, the lady moved slowly up the room. Seen now, in broad daylight, she looked tall, fair and shapely; on each of her temples her hair, of a very dark brown, was clustered in round curls; her dress was of purple cloth, relieved by a sort of Spanish trimming of black velvet; a gold watch shone at her girdle. Let the reader add, to complete the picture, refined features, and a stately air and carriage, and he will have a correct idea of the exterior of Miss Temple.

The superintendent of Lowood (for such was this lady), having taken her seat before a pair of globes, summoned the first class round her, and commenced giving a lesson in geography; the lower classes were called by the teachers: repetitions in history, grammar, etc., went on till the clock at last struck twelve. The superintendent rose.

"I have a word to address to the pupils," said she. "You had this morning a breakfast which you could not eat; you must be hungry—I have ordered that a lunch of bread and cheese shall be served."

The teachers looked at her with a sort of surprise.

"It is to be done on my responsibility," she added, in an explanatory tone to them, and immediately left the room.

The bread and cheese was presently brought in and distributed, to the high delight of the whole school. The order was now given, "To the garden!" Each put on a coarse straw bonnet and a cloak of gray frieze. I was similarly equipped, and, following the stream, I made my way into the open air.

The garden was a wide enclosure, surrounded with high walls; a covered veranda ran down one side, and broad walks bordered a middle space. Now, at the latter end of January, all was wintry blight and brown decay. I shuddered as I stood and looked round me. The stronger of the girls ran about and engaged in active games, but sundry pale and thin ones herded together for shelter and warmth in the veranda; and among these I heard frequently the sound of a hollow cough.

As yet I had spoken to no one, nor did anybody seem to take notice of me; I was accustomed to isolation; it did not oppress me much. I leaned against a pillar of the veranda, and, trying to forget the cold, delivered myself up to watching and thinking. I looked up at the house: a large building, half of which seemed gray and old, the other half quite new. The new part was lit by mullioned windows; a tablet over the door bore this inscription:

LOWOOD INSTITUTION. This portion was rebuilt A.D. —— by Naomi Brocklehurst, of Brocklehurst Hall. *Let your light so shine before men, that they may see your good works, and glorify your Father which is in heaven.*—St. Matt. V. 16.

I read these words over and over. I was pondering the significance of "Institution," and endeavoring to make out a connection between the first words and the verse of Scripture, when the sound of a cough behind me made me turn my head. I saw a girl sitting on a stone bench, intent over a book; I could see the title, *Rasselas*, a name that struck me as strange and attractive. In turning a leaf she happened to look up, and I said to her:

"Is your book interesting?"

"I like it," she answered, after a pause, during which she examined me.

"What is it about?" I continued.

"You may look at it," replied the girl, offering me the book.

I did so; a brief examination convinced me that the contents were less taking than the title. *Rasselas* looked dull to my trifling taste; I saw nothing about fairies, about genii.

I returned it to her, and again I ventured to speak. "Can you tell me what that writing over the door means? What is Lowood Institution?"

"This house where you are come to live."

"And why do they call it Institution? Is it in any way different from other schools?"

"It is partly a charity school: you and I, and all the rest of us, are charity children. I suppose you are an orphan; are not either your father or your mother dead?"

"Both died before I can remember."

"Well, all the girls here have lost one or both parents, and this is called an institution for educating orphans."

"Do we pay no money?"

"We pay, or our friends pay, fifteen pounds a year for each."

"Then why do they call us charity children?"

"Because fifteen pounds is not enough for board and teaching, and the deficiency is supplied by subscription."

"Who was Naomi Brocklehurst?"

"The lady who built the new part of this house and whose son oversees everything here."

"Then this house does not belong to that tall lady who wears a watch and who said we were to have some bread and cheese."

"To Miss Temple? Oh, no! I wish it did. She has to answer to Mr. Brocklehurst for all she does."

"Does he live here?"

"No—two miles off, at a large hall."

"Is he a good man?"

"He is a clergyman and is said to do a great deal of good."

"What are the other teachers called?"

"The one with red cheeks is called Miss Smith; the little one with black hair is Miss Scatcherd; and the one who wears a shawl is Madame Pierrot—she comes from France, and teaches French."

"Are you happy here?"

"You ask rather too many questions. I have given you answers enough for the present. Now I want to read."

But at that moment the summons sounded for dinner; all

re-entered the house. After dinner, which was scarcely more appetizing than breakfast, we immediately adjourned to the schoolroom; lessons recommenced, and were continued till five o'clock.

The only marked event of the afternoon was that I saw the girl with whom I had conversed in the veranda dismissed in disgrace by Miss Scatcherd from a history class and sent to stand in the middle of the large schoolroom. The punishment seemed to me in a high degree ignominious, especially for so great a girl—she looked thirteen or upward. I expected she would show signs of great distress and shame; but to my surprise she neither wept nor blushed: composed, though grave, she stood, the central mark of all eyes. How can she bear it so quietly—so firmly? I asked of myself. Were I in her place, it seems to me I should wish the earth to open and swallow me up. I wonder what sort of a girl she is—whether good or naughty.

Soon after five p.m. we had another meal, consisting of a small mug of coffee and half a slice of brown bread. I devoured my bread and drank my coffee with relish, but I should have been glad of as much more. Half an hour's recreation succeeded, then study; then the glass of water and the piece of oatcake, prayers and bed. Such was my first day at Lowood.

THE NEXT DAY COMMENCED as before, getting up and dressing by rushlight. During its course I was enrolled a member of the fourth class, and regular tasks and occupations were assigned me. At first, being little accustomed to learn by heart, the lessons appeared to me both long and difficult; and I was glad when, about three o'clock in the afternoon, Miss Smith put into my hands a border of muslin two yards long, together with needle, thimble, etc., and sent me to sit in a quiet corner, with directions to hem the same. At that hour most of the others were sewing likewise; but one class still stood round Miss Scatcherd's chair. The lesson was English history. Among the pupils I observed my acquaintance of the veranda. She answered every question correctly.

I kept expecting Miss Scatcherd to praise her; instead, Miss Scatcherd continued to make her an object of constant notice. She was continually addressing to her such phrases as the following:

"Burns—" the girls were all called by their surnames "—Burns, you are standing on the side of your shoe; turn your toes out immediately." "Burns, you poke your chin most unpleasantly; draw it in." "Burns, hold your head up."

My attention was now called off by Miss Smith desiring me to hold a skein of thread; when I returned to my seat Miss Scatcherd was just delivering an order; Burns left the class, and, going into a small inner room, returned carrying a bundle of twigs tied together at one end. This ominous tool she presented to Miss Scatcherd with a respectful curtsy; then she quietly unloosed her pinafore, and the teacher instantly and sharply inflicted on her neck a dozen strokes with the bunch of twigs. Not a tear rose to Burns' eye; and, while I paused from my sewing, quivering at this spectacle with impotent anger, not a feature of her pensive face altered its expression.

"Hardened girl!" exclaimed Miss Scatcherd; "nothing can correct you of your slatternly habits. Carry the rod away."

Burns obeyed; I looked at her narrowly as she emerged from the inner room; the trace of a tear glistened on her thin cheek.

The play hour in the evening I thought the pleasantest fraction of the day at Lowood: the long restraint of the day was slackened; the schoolroom felt warmer than in the morning—its fires being allowed to burn more brightly to supply, in some measure, the place of candles, not yet introduced. On that evening I wandered among the laughing groups and made my way to one of the fireplaces; there, kneeling by the fender, I found Burns, abstracted from all round her by the companionship of a book.

"It is still *Rasselas?*" I asked, coming behind her.

"Yes," she said, "and I have just finished it."

She shut it up. I sat down by her on the floor.

"What is your name besides Burns?"

"Helen."

"Do you come a long way from here?"

"I come from a place up north, on the borders of Scotland."

"You must wish to leave Lowood?"

"No; why should I? I was sent to Lowood to get an education, and it would be of no use going away until I have attained that object."

"But that teacher, Miss Scatcherd, is so cruel to you."

"Cruel? Not at all! She is severe; she dislikes my faults."

"If I were in your place I should dislike her; I should resist her; if she struck me with that rod, I should get it from her and break it."

"Probably you would do nothing of the sort; but if you did, Mr. Brocklehurst would expel you; that would be a great grief to your relations. It is far better to endure patiently a smart which nobody feels but yourself than to commit a hasty action whose evil consequences will extend to all connected with you; and, besides, the Bible bids us to return good for evil."

I heard her with wonder: I felt that Helen Burns considered things by a light invisible to my eyes.

"You say you have faults, Helen. What are they? To me you seem very good."

"Then learn from me not to judge by appearances. I am, as Miss Scatcherd said, slatternly; I am careless; I forget rules; I have no method. This is all very provoking to Miss Scatcherd, who is naturally neat and particular."

"Is Miss Temple as severe to you as Miss Scatcherd?"

At the utterance of Miss Temple's name, a soft smile flitted over her grave face. "Miss Temple is full of goodness. It pains her to be severe to anyone; she sees my errors, and tells me of them gently."

"I would be good with her, then. It is all I ever desire to be— to be good to those who are good to me. But if people are always kind and obedient to those who are cruel and unjust, the wicked people have it all their own way: they never feel afraid, and so they grow worse and worse."

"It is not violence that best overcomes hate."

"What then?"

"Read the New Testament, and observe what Christ says: love your enemies; bless them that curse you; do good to them that hate you and despitefully use you."

"Then I should love Mrs. Reed, which I cannot do; I should bless her son John, which is impossible."

In her turn, Helen Burns asked me to explain; and I proceeded forthwith to pour out the tale of my sufferings and resentments. Helen heard me patiently to the end, but she said nothing.

"Well," I asked, "is not Mrs. Reed a hardhearted, bad woman?"

"She has been unkind to you, no doubt; but how minutely you remember all she has done! Would you not be happier if you tried to forget her severity? Life appears to me too short to be spent in nursing animosity. We are, one and all, burdened with faults in this world; but the time will soon come when, I trust, we shall put them off in putting off our corruptible bodies; when sin will fall from us, and only the spark of the spirit will remain, pure as when it left the Creator!"

Helen's head, always drooping, sank lower. I saw by her look she wished no longer to talk to me, but rather to converse with her own thoughts. She was not allowed much time for meditation. A monitor, a great rough girl, presently came up, exclaiming:

"Helen Burns, if you don't go and put your drawer in order this minute, I'll tell Miss Scatcherd to come look at it!"

Helen sighed as her reverie fled and, getting up, obeyed the monitor without delay.

CHAPTER IV

MY FIRST QUARTER AT LOWOOD seemed an age; it comprised an irksome struggle with new rules and unwonted tasks. The fear of failure in these points harassed me worse than the physical hardships of my lot, though these were no trifles.

During January, February and part of March, the deep snows and almost impassable roads prevented our stirring beyond the garden walls, except to go to church; but within these limits we had to pass an hour every day in the open air. Our clothing was insufficient to protect us from the severe cold; we had no boots, the snow got into our shoes, our ungloved hands became covered with chilblains, as were our feet. Then the scanty supply of food was distressing; with the keen appetites of growing children, we had scarcely sufficient to keep alive a delicate invalid.

I have not yet alluded to the visits of Mr. Brocklehurst, and indeed that gentleman was away from home during the greater part of the first month after my arrival. I need not say that I had my own reasons for dreading his coming, but come he did at last.

One afternoon as I was sitting with a slate in my hand, puzzling over a sum, my eyes, raised in abstraction to the window, caught sight of a figure just passing. I recognized almost instinctively that gaunt outline; and when, two minutes after, all the school rose en masse, it was not necessary for me to look up in order to ascertain whose entrance they thus greeted. A long stride measured the schoolroom, and presently beside Miss Temple stood the same black column which had frowned on me so ominously from the hearthrug of Gateshead.

I had my own reasons for being dismayed at this apparition: too well I remembered the promise pledged by Mr. Brocklehurst to apprise Miss Temple and the teachers of my vicious nature. He stood now at Miss Temple's side, speaking in her ear. I did not doubt he was making disclosures of my villainy, and I watched her eye with painful anxiety, expecting every moment to see it turn on me with contempt. I listened too; and as I happened to be seated at the top of the room, I caught most of what he said; its import relieved me from immediate apprehension.

"I suppose, Miss Temple, the thread I bought at Lowton will do; it struck me that it would be just of the quality for the calico chemises, and I sorted the needles to match. You may tell Miss Smith that I forgot to make a memorandum of the darning needles, but she shall have some sent in next week; and she is not, on any account, to give out more than one at a time to each pupil; if they have more, they are apt to be careless and lose them."

"Your directions shall be attended to, Mr. Brocklehurst," said Miss Temple.

"And, ma'am," he continued, "I find, in settling accounts, that a lunch of bread and cheese has twice been served to the girls during the past fortnight. How is this? Who introduced this innovation?"

"I am responsible, sir," replied Miss Temple. "The breakfast was so ill-prepared that the pupils could not eat it; and I dared not allow them to fast till dinner time."

"Madam, allow me an instant. You are aware that my plan in bringing up these girls is to render them hardy, patient, self-denying. Should any little accidental disappointment of the appetite occur, such as the spoiling of a meal, the incident ought not to be neutralized by replacing with something more delicate the comfort lost, thus pampering the body. A brief address on those occasions would not be mistimed, wherein a judicious instructor would take the opportunity of referring to the sufferings of the primitive Christians; to the exhortations of our blessed Lord Himself, calling upon His disciples to take up their cross and follow Him."

Mr. Brocklehurst paused. Miss Temple gazed straight before her, and her face, naturally pale as marble, appeared to be assuming also the coldness and fixity of that material. Meantime Mr. Brocklehurst surveyed the whole school. Suddenly his eye gave a blink, as if it had met something that shocked it; turning, he said in rapid accents:

"Miss Temple, what—*what* is that girl with curled hair? Red hair, ma'am, curled—curled all over?" And extending his cane he pointed to the awful object.

"It is Julia Severn," replied Miss Temple, very quietly.

"Julia Severn, ma'am! And why has she curled hair, in defiance of every precept and principle of this house?"

"Julia's hair curls naturally," returned Miss Temple, still more quietly.

"Naturally! Yes, but we are not to conform to nature; I wish these girls to be the children of Grace, with hair arranged modestly, plainly. Miss Temple, that girl's hair must be cut off entirely. I will send a barber tomorrow!"

Mr. Brocklehurst was here interrupted: three other visitors, ladies, entered the room. They were splendidly attired in velvet, silk and furs; the two younger (fine girls of sixteen and seventeen) had hats, shaded with ostrich plumes, and from under the brims of this headdress fell a profusion of light tresses, elaborately curled; the elderly lady was enveloped in a velvet shawl trimmed with ermine, and she wore a false front of French curls. These ladies were deferentially received by Miss Temple as Mrs. and Misses Brocklehurst, and conducted to seats of honor at the top of the room. Having previously rummaged through the rooms upstairs, they now proceeded to address divers reproofs to Miss Smith, who was charged with the care of the linen and of the dormitories. But I had no time to listen to what they said; other matters enchained my attention.

Hitherto, I had not neglected precautions to secure my personal safety and elude observation. To this end, I had sat well back on the form, and while seeming to be busy with my sum, had held my slate so as to conceal my face. I might have escaped notice, had not my treacherous slate somehow slipped from my hand, and falling with a crash, directly drawn every eye upon me. I knew it was all over now, and, as I stooped to pick up the two fragments of slate, I rallied my forces for the worst. It came.

"A careless girl!" said Mr. Brocklehurst and, immediately after, "It is the new pupil, I perceive." And before I could draw breath, "I must not forget I have a word to say respecting her." Then aloud (how loud it seemed to me!), "Let the child who broke her slate come forward!"

Of my own accord I could not have stirred: I was paralyzed; but the two great girls who sat on each side of me set me on my legs and pushed me towards the dread judge, and then Miss Temple gently assisted me to his very feet, and I caught her whispered counsel, "Don't be afraid, Jane. I saw it was an accident; you shall not be punished."

The kind whisper went to my heart like a dagger.

"Fetch that stool," said Mr. Brocklehurst, pointing to a high one; it was brought.

"Place the child upon it."

And I was placed there, by whom I don't know: I was only

aware that I was hoisted to the height of Mr. Brocklehurst's nose, and that he was within a yard of me.

Mr. Brocklehurst hemmed. "Ladies," said he, turning to his family, "Miss Temple, teachers and children, you all see this girl? You see she is yet young; you observe she possesses the ordinary form of childhood. Who would think that the Evil One had already found a servant in her? Yet such, I grieve to say, is the case."

A pause—in which I began to steady the palsy of my nerves, and to feel that the trial must be firmly sustained.

"My dear children," pursued the black-marble clergyman, with pathos, "this is a melancholy occasion, for it becomes my duty to warn you that this girl, who might be one of God's own lambs, is a little castaway. You must be on your guard against her; if necessary, avoid her company. Teachers, you must watch her; punish her body to save her soul, if, indeed, such salvation be possible, for (my tongue falters while I tell it) this girl, the native of a Christian land, worse than many a little heathen who says its prayers to Brahma—this girl is—a liar!"

Now came a pause, during which the female Brocklehursts whispered, "How shocking!" Mr. Brocklehurst resumed.

"This I learned from the charitable lady who adopted her, reared her as her own, and whose kindness the unhappy girl repaid by an ingratitude so dreadful that at last her patroness was obliged to separate her from her own young ones, fearful lest her vicious example should contaminate them; she has sent her here to be healed, even as the Jews of old sent their diseased to the troubled pool of Bethesda; and, teachers, superintendent, I beg of you not to allow the waters to stagnate round her."

With this sublime conclusion, Mr. Brocklehurst adjusted the top button of his surtout, muttered something to his family, who rose, bowed to Miss Temple, and then all the great people sailed in state from the room. Turning at the door, my judge said:

"Let her stand half an hour longer on that stool, and let no one speak to her during the remainder of the day."

There was I, then, mounted aloft; I, who had said I could not bear the shame of standing on my feet in the middle of the room, was now exposed to general view on a pedestal of infamy. What my sensations were no language can describe, but just as they all rose to stifle my breath, a girl came up and passed me; in passing, she lifted her eyes. What a light inspired them! What an extraordinary sensation that ray sent through me! It was as if a martyr, a hero, had passed a slave or victim, and imparted strength in the transit. I lifted up my head and took a firm stand on the stool. Helen Burns asked some slight question about her work of Miss Smith, returned to her place and smiled at me as she again went by. What a smile! I remember it now, and I know that it was the effluence of true courage; it lit up her thin face like a reflection from the aspect of an angel.

ERE THE HALF HOUR ENDED, five o'clock struck; school was dismissed, and all were gone into the refectory to tea. I now ventured to descend. It was dusk; I retired into a corner and sat down on the floor. Reaction took place, and soon, so overwhelming was the grief that seized me, I sank prostrate with my face to the ground, my tears watering the boards. I had meant to be so good, and to do so much at Lowood: to earn respect and win affection. Already I had made progress: that very morning I had reached the head of my class; Miss Miller had praised me warmly; Miss Temple had smiled approbation; now, here I lay again crushed and trodden on; and could I ever rise more?

Never, I thought; and ardently I wished to die. While I sobbed out this wish, someone approached. I started up—again Helen Burns was near me; she brought my coffee and bread.

"Come, eat something," she said, and she sat down on the ground near me, embracing her knees with her arms; in that attitude she remained silent as an Indian. I was the first who spoke:

"Helen, why do you stay with a girl whom everybody believes to be a liar?"

"Everybody, Jane? Why, there are only eighty people who have heard you called so, and the world contains hundreds of millions."

"But what have I to do with millions? The eighty I know despise me."

"Jane, you are mistaken: probably not one in the school either despises or dislikes you; many, I am sure, pity you."

"How can they pity me after what Mr. Brocklehurst said?"

"Mr. Brocklehurst is not a god; he is little liked here. Had he treated you as a favorite, you would have found enemies all around you; as it is, the greater number would offer you sympathy if they dared. Besides, Jane—" She paused.

"Well, Helen?" said I, putting my hand into hers; she chafed my fingers gently to warm them, and went on, "If all the world hated you and believed you wicked, while your own conscience approved you and absolved you from guilt, you would not be without friends."

"No; I know I should think well of myself; but that is not enough. If others don't love me, I would rather die than live."

"Hush, Jane! You think too much of the love of human beings; you are too impulsive; the sovereign hand that created your frame has provided you with other resources than your feeble self. Besides this earth, and the race of men, there is an invisible world. Why, then, should we ever sink overwhelmed with distress, when life is so soon over, and death is so certain an entrance to happiness—to glory?"

I was silent: Helen had calmed me; but in the tranquillity she imparted there was an alloy of inexpressible sadness. When, having done speaking, she breathed a little fast and coughed, I momentarily forgot my own sorrows to yield to a vague concern for her. Resting my head on her shoulder, I put my arms round her waist. Then another person came in, whom we at once recognized as Miss Temple.

"I came on purpose to find you, Jane Eyre," said she; "I want you in my room; and as Helen Burns is with you, she may come too."

We went; following the superintendent's guidance, we threaded some intricate passages before we reached her apartment; it contained a good fire and looked cheerful. Miss Temple told Helen Burns to be seated in a low armchair on one side of the hearth, and herself taking another, she called me to her side.

"Is it all over?" she asked, looking down at my face. "Have you cried your grief away?"

"I am afraid I never shall do that."

"Why?"

"Because I have been wrongly accused; and you, ma'am, and everybody else will now think me wicked."

"We shall think you what you prove yourself to be, my child. Continue to act as a good girl, and you will satisfy me."

"Shall I, Miss Temple?"

"You will," said she, passing her arm round me. "And now tell me who is the lady whom Mr. Brocklehurst called your benefactress?"

"Mrs. Reed, my uncle's wife. My uncle is dead, and he left me to her care."

"Well now, Jane, you know that when a criminal is accused, he is always allowed to speak in his own defense. You have been charged with falsehood; defend yourself to me as well as you can."

I resolved, in the depth of my heart, that I would be most moderate; and, having reflected a few minutes, I told her all the story of my sad childhood. In the course of the tale I had mentioned Mr. Lloyd as having come to see me after the fit: for I never forgot the, to me, frightful episode of the red room. Exhausted by emotion, my language was subdued; and mindful of Helen's warnings against the indulgence of resentment, I infused into the narrative far less of gall and wormwood than ordinary. Thus restrained and simplified, it sounded more credible: I felt that Miss Temple believed me. When I had finished, she regarded me a few minutes in silence; she then said:

"I know something of Mr. Lloyd; I shall write to him. If his reply agrees with your statement, you shall be publicly cleared from every imputation; to me, Jane, you are clear now."

She kissed me, and still keeping me at her side, she proceeded to address Helen Burns.

"How are you tonight, Helen? Have you coughed much today?"

"Not quite so much I think, ma'am."

"And the pain in your chest?"

"It is a little better."

Miss Temple got up, took her hand and examined her pulse; then I heard her sigh low. She was pensive a few minutes, then rousing herself, she said cheerfully, "But you two are my visitors tonight; I must treat you as such." She rang the bell. "Barbara," she said to the servant who answered it, "I have not yet had tea; bring the tray, and place cups for these two young ladies."

And a tray was soon brought. How pretty, to my eyes, did the bright teapot look, placed on the little table near the fire! How fragrant was the steam of the beverage, and the scent of the toast, of which, however, I to my dismay (for I was beginning to be hungry) discerned only a very small portion; Miss Temple discerned it too; and said, smiling, "Fortunately, I have it in my power to supply deficiencies for this once."

Having invited Helen and me to approach the table, and placed before each of us a cup of tea, she got up, unlocked a drawer, and disclosed to our eyes a good-sized seedcake. "I meant to give each of you some of this to take with you," said she, "but as there is so little toast, you must have it now," and she proceeded to cut slices with a generous hand.

We feasted that evening as on nectar and ambrosia; and not the least delight of the entertainment was the smile of gratification with which our hostess regarded us as we satisfied our appetites on the fare she liberally supplied. Tea over, we sat one on each side of her, and now a conversation followed between her and Helen which it was indeed a privilege to hear. But soon the bell announced bedtime: no delay could be admitted. Miss Temple embraced us both, saying, "God bless you, my children!"

Helen she held a little longer than me; it was Helen her eye followed to the door; it was for her she a second time breathed a sad sigh.

ABOUT A WEEK SUBSEQUENTLY to the incidents above narrated, Miss Temple, who had written to Mr. Lloyd, received his answer; it appeared that what he said went to corroborate my account. Miss Temple, having assembled the whole school, announced that inquiry had been made into the charges alleged against Jane Eyre, and that she was most happy to be able to pronounce her cleared from every imputation. The teachers then shook hands with me, and a murmur of pleasure ran through the ranks of my companions.

Thus relieved of a grievous load, I from that hour set to work afresh. I toiled hard, and my success was proportionate to my efforts; in a few weeks I was promoted to a higher class; in less than two months I was allowed to commence French and drawing. I would not now have exchanged Lowood, with all its privations, for Gateshead and its daily luxuries.

But the hardships of Lowood lessened. Spring drew on; the frosts of winter ceased. My wretched feet, flayed and swollen by the sharp air of January, began to heal. In the garden, flowers peeped out among the leaves: snowdrops, crocuses and golden-eyed pansies. On Thursday afternoons we now took walks, and found still sweeter flowers opening under the hedges.

And I discovered, too, that a great pleasure lay all outside the high and spike-guarded walls of our garden: this pleasure consisted in prospect of noble summits girdling a great hill hollow, rich in verdure and shadow, in a bright beck, full of dark stones and sparkling eddies.

April advanced to May: a bright, serene May it was, days of blue sky and placid sunshine. Vegetation matured with vigor; Lowood became all green, all flowery; its great elm, ash and oak skeletons were restored to majestic life; unnumbered varieties of moss filled its hollows.

All this I began to enjoy often and fully, free, unwatched, and almost alone; for this unwonted liberty and pleasure there was a cause, to which it now becomes my task to advert.

Have I not described a pleasant site for Lowood, when I speak of it as bosomed in hill and wood, and rising from the verge of a stream? Assuredly, pleasant enough, but whether healthy or not is another question.

That forest dell was the cradle of fog and pestilence, which, quickening with the quickening spring, crept into the orphan

Helen was ill at present: for some weeks she had been removed from my sight. She was not, I was told, in the hospital portion of the house, for her complaint was consumption, not typhus; and by consumption I, in my ignorance, understood something mild, which time and care would be sure to alleviate.

One evening in June, I had stayed out very late with Mary Ann in the wood; we had separated ourselves from the others, and had wandered far, so far that we lost our way, and had to ask it at a lonely cottage. When we got back, it was after moonrise; a pony, which we knew to be the surgeon's, was standing at the door. Mary Ann remarked that she supposed someone must be very ill, as Mr. Bates had been sent for at that time of the evening. She went into the house; I stayed behind a few minutes to linger in the garden: the flowers smelled so sweet as the dew fell; it was such a pleasant evening, so serene, so warm; the still glowing west promised another fine day on the morrow. I was noting these things and enjoying them as a child might, when it entered my mind as it had never done before:

How sad to be lying now on a sickbed, and to be in danger of dying! This world is pleasant—it would be dreary to be called from it, and to have to go who knows where?

And then my mind made its first earnest effort to comprehend what had been infused into it concerning heaven and hell; it recoiled, baffled. While pondering, I heard the front door open; Mr. Bates came out, and with him was a nurse. After she had seen him mount his horse and depart, she was about to close the door, but I ran up to her.

"How is Helen Burns?"

"Very poorly," was the answer.

"Is it she whom Mr. Bates has been to see?"

"Yes."

"And what does he say about her?"

"He says she'll not be here long."

This phrase, uttered in my hearing yesterday, would have only conveyed the notion that she was about to be removed to her own home. I should not have suspected that it meant she was asylum, breathed typhus through its crowded rooms, and, ere May arrived, transformed the seminary into a hospital.

Semistarvation and neglected colds had predisposed most of the pupils to receive infection: forty-five out of the eighty girls lay ill at one time. Classes were broken up, rules relaxed. The few who continued well were allowed almost unlimited license because the medical attendant insisted on exercise to keep them in health, and no one had leisure to watch them. Miss Temple's whole attention was absorbed by the patients, and the teachers were occupied with making preparations for the departure of those girls who were fortunate enough to have friends and relations able to remove them from the seat of contagion. Many, already smitten, went home only to die; some died at the school, and were buried quietly and quickly.

While disease had thus become an inhabitant of Lowood, and death its frequent visitor, that bright May shone unclouded over the hills and beautiful woodland out of doors. I, and the rest who continued well, enjoyed fully the beauties of the scene and season. They let us ramble in the wood, like gypsies, from morning till night; we lived better too. The cross housekeeper was gone, driven away by the fear of infection; her successor, unused to the ways of her new abode, provided with comparative liberality. Besides, there were fewer to feed: the sick could eat little; when there was no time to prepare a dinner, which often happened, she would give us a large piece of cold pie, and this we carried away with us to the wood, where we each chose the spot we liked best, and dined sumptuously.

My favorite seat was a broad stone, rising white and dry from the very middle of the beck, and only to be got at by wading through the water, a feat I accomplished barefoot. The stone was just broad enough to accommodate, comfortably, another girl and me, at that time my chosen comrade—one Mary Ann Wilson: a shrewd, observant personage, witty and original, whose society I took pleasure in.

And where, meantime, was Helen Burns? Why did I not spend these sweet days of liberty with her?

dying, but I knew instantly now; it opened clear to me that Helen Burns was numbering her last days in this world. I experienced a shock of horror, then a strong thrill of grief, then a desire—a necessity—to see her; and I asked in what room she lay.

"She is in Miss Temple's room," said the nurse.

"May I go up and speak to her?"

"Oh, no, child! It is not likely. Now come in; you'll catch the fever if you stop out when the dew is falling."

I went in, and the nurse closed the door. I was just in time; it was nine o'clock, and Miss Miller was calling the pupils to go to bed. Two hours later, probably near eleven, not having been able to fall asleep, I rose softly in the silent dormitory, put on my frock over my nightdress, and, without shoes, crept off in quest of Miss Temple's room. I dreaded being discovered and sent back; for I *must* see Helen before she died—I must give her one last kiss, exchange with her one last word.

I reached Miss Temple's room. A light shone from under the door, and coming near, I found the door ajar—probably to admit fresh air. Full of impatient impulses I put it back and looked in. My eye sought Helen, and feared to find death.

Close by Miss Temple's bed, half covered with its white curtains, stood a little crib; I saw the outline of a form under the clothes. The nurse I had spoken to in the garden sat in an easy chair, asleep. Miss Temple was not to be seen: I knew afterwards that she had been called to a delirious patient in the fever room. I advanced; then paused by the crib side. I still recoiled at the dread of seeing a corpse.

"Helen?" I whispered softly; "are you awake?"

She stirred herself, put back the curtain, and I saw her face, pale, wasted, but quite composed; she looked so little changed that my fear was instantly dissipated.

"Can it be you, Jane?" she asked in her own gentle voice.

Oh! I thought, she is not going to die; they are mistaken: she could not speak and look so calmly if she were.

I got on to her crib and kissed her; her forehead was cold, and her cheek both cold and thin; but she smiled as of old.

"Why are you come here, Jane? It is past eleven o'clock."

"I came to see you, Helen; I heard you were very ill, and I could not sleep till I had spoken to you."

"You came to bid me good-by, then; you are just in time probably."

"Are you going somewhere, Helen? Are you going home?"

"Yes; to my long home—my last home."

"No, no, Helen!" I stopped, distressed. While I tried to devour my tears, a fit of coughing seized Helen; it did not, however, wake the nurse; when it was over, she lay some minutes exhausted; then she whispered:

"Jane, your feet are bare; lie down and cover yourself with my quilt."

I did so: she put her arm over me, and I nestled close to her. After a long silence, she resumed, still whispering:

"I am very happy, Jane; and when you hear that I am dead, you must be sure and not grieve. We all must die one day, and the illness which is removing me is gentle and gradual: my mind is at rest. I leave no one to regret me much: I have only a father; and he is lately married, and will not miss me. By dying young, I shall escape great sufferings."

"But where are you going to, Helen? Can you see? Do you know?"

"I believe; I have faith: I am going to God."

"You are sure, then, Helen, that there is such a place as heaven; and that our souls can get to it when we die?"

"I am sure there is a future state; I can resign my immortal part to God without any misgiving. God is my father; God is my friend: I love Him; I believe He loves me."

"And shall I see you again, Helen, when I die?"

"You will come to the same region of happiness, be received by the same mighty, universal Parent, no doubt, dear Jane."

I clasped my arms closer round Helen; she seemed dearer to me than ever; I felt as if I could not let her go. Presently she said in the sweetest tone:

"How comfortable I am! That last fit of coughing has tired me a little; I feel as if I could sleep. But don't leave me, Jane; I like to have you near me."

"I'll stay with you, *dear* Helen; no one shall take me away."

"Are you warm, darling?"

"Yes."

"Good night, Jane."

"Good night, Helen."

She kissed me, and I her; and we both soon slumbered.

When I awoke it was day; an unusual movement roused me. I was in somebody's arms; the nurse held me; she was carrying me through the passage back to the dormitory. I was not reprimanded for leaving my bed; people had something else to think about. No explanation was afforded then to my many questions; but a day or two afterwards I learned that Miss Temple, on returning to her own room at dawn, had found me laid in the little crib, my face against Helen Burns's shoulder, my arms round her neck. I was asleep, and Helen was dead.

CHAPTER V

HITHERTO I HAVE RECORDED in detail the events of my insignificant existence; to the first ten years of my life I have given several chapters. But this is not to be a regular autobiography: therefore I now pass a space of eight years almost in silence; a few lines only are necessary to keep up the links of connection.

When the typhus fever had fulfilled its mission of devastation at Lowood, it disappeared from thence, but not till the number of its victims had drawn public attention to the school. Inquiry was made into the origin of the scourge, and facts came out which excited public indignation in a high degree. Several benevolent individuals subscribed for the erection of a building in a better situation; improvements in diet and clothing were introduced; the funds of the school were entrusted to the management of a committee. Mr. Brocklehurst, who, because of his wealth and family connections, could not be overlooked, still retained the post of treasurer; but he was aided in his duties by gentlemen of rather more enlarged and sympathizing minds. The school, thus improved, became in time a truly useful and noble institution. I remained an inmate of its walls, after its regeneration, for eight years: six as pupil, and two as teacher; and in both capacities I bear my testimony to its value and importance.

During those eight years my life was uniform, but not unhappy. In time I rose to be the first girl of the first class; then I was invested with the office of teacher, which I discharged with zeal for two years; but at the end of that time I altered.

Miss Temple, through all changes, had thus far continued superintendent of the seminary; her friendship and society had been my continual solace: she had stood me in the stead of mother, governess and, latterly, companion. At this period she married, removed with her husband (a clergyman, an excellent man, almost worthy of such a wife) to a distant county, and consequently was lost to me.

From the day she left I was no longer the same: with her was gone every settled feeling, every association that had made Lowood in some degree a home to me. I had imbibed from her something of her nature and much of her habits: what seemed better regulated feelings had become the inmates of my mind. But destiny, in the shape of the Reverend Mr. Nasmyth, came between me and Miss Temple: I saw her in her traveling dress step into a post chaise, shortly after the marriage ceremony, then retired to my room, and there spent in solitude the greatest part of the half-holiday granted in honor of the occasion.

I walked about the chamber most of the time. I imagined myself only to be regretting my loss; but when my reflections were concluded, and evening was far advanced, it dawned on me that in the interval I had undergone a transforming process; that my mind had put off all it had borrowed of Miss Temple— and that now I was beginning to feel the stirring of old emotions. It was as if the reason for my tranquillity was gone. My world had for some years been in Lowood: my experience had been of its rules and systems; now I remembered that the real world was wide, and that a varied field of hopes and fears, of sensations and excitements, awaited those who had courage to go forth into its expanse.

I opened my window, looked out. My eye passed all other objects to rest on the hilly horizon, the blue peaks: it was those I longed to surmount. I traced the white road winding round the base of one mountain and vanishing in a gorge between two: how I longed to follow it further! An age seemed to have elapsed since the day which brought me first to Lowood, and I had never quitted it since. My vacations had all been spent at school; neither Mrs. Reed nor any of her family had ever been to visit me. I had had no communication by letter or message with the outer world: school rules, school habits and notions—such was what I knew of existence. And now I felt that it was not enough. I desired liberty; for liberty I uttered a prayer.

Here a bell, ringing the hour of supper, called me downstairs.

I was not free to resume the interrupted chain of my reflections till bedtime: even then a teacher who occupied the same room with me kept me from the subject by prolonged small talk. Miss Gryce—she was a heavy Welshwoman—snored at last; I was debarrassed of interruption; I sat up in bed by way of arousing my brain, and then I proceeded *to think* again with all my might.

"What do I want? A new place, new employment, new faces, under new circumstances. How do people do to get a new place? They apply to friends, I suppose; I have no friends. There are many others who have no friends; what is their resource?"

I could not tell; but as I lay down again the answer came quietly to my mind: "Those who want situations advertise; you must advertise in the ——shire *Herald*."

"How? I know nothing about advertising."

Replies rose smooth and prompt now:

"You must enclose the advertisement and the money to pay for it under a cover directed to the editor of the *Herald;* you must post it at Lowton; answers must be addressed to J.E. at the post office there; you can go and inquire in about a week after you send your letter, if any are come, and act accordingly."

This scheme I went over in my mind. When I had it in a clear practical form, I felt satisfied and fell asleep.

With earliest day, I was up; I had my advertisement written before the bell rang to rouse the school; it ran thus:

A young lady accustomed to tuition is desirous of meeting with a situation in a family where the children are under fourteen [I thought that as I was barely eighteen, it would not do to undertake the guidance of pupils nearer my own age]. She is qualified to teach the usual branches of a good English education, together with French, drawing and music. Address J.E., Post Office, Lowton, ——shire.

After tea, I asked leave of the new superintendent to go to Lowton; permission was readily granted. It was a walk of two miles, but the days were still long; I visited a shop or two, slipped the letter into the post office, and came back with a relieved heart.

The succeeding week seemed long; it came to an end at last, however, and once more I found myself afoot on the road to Lowton. My ostensible errand on this occasion was to get measured for a pair of shoes; so I discharged that business first, and when it was done, I stepped across the little street to the post office. It was kept by an old dame, who wore horn spectacles on her nose and black mittens on her hands.

"Are there any letters for J.E.?" I asked.

She peered at me over her spectacles, and then she opened a drawer and fumbled among its contents for a long time, so long that my hopes began to falter. At last, having held a document before her glasses for nearly five minutes, she presented it across the counter—it was for J.E.

I put it in my pocket and turned my face homeward. I could not open it then; rules obliged me to be back by eight, and it was already half past seven. Various duties awaited me on my arrival, and it was not until we finally retired for the night, and Miss Gryce was snoring, that I took out my letter. The contents were brief.

If J.E., who advertised in the ——*shire Herald*, is in a position to give satisfactory references as to character and competency, a situation can be offered her where there is but one pupil, a little girl, under ten years of age; and where the salary is thirty pounds per annum. J.E. is requested to send references, name, address and all particulars to: Mrs. Fairfax, Thornfield, near Millcote, ——shire.

I examined the document long; the writing was old-fashioned and rather uncertain, like that of an elderly lady. I felt that an elderly lady was no bad ingredient in the business I had on hand. Mrs. Fairfax! I saw her in a black gown and widow's cap; a model of elderly English respectability. Thornfield! That, doubtless, was the name of her house: a neat, orderly spot, I was sure. Millcote—I brushed up my recollections of the map of England; Millcote was seventy miles nearer London than the remote county where I now resided. It was a large manufacturing town on the banks of the A——.

Next day new steps were to be taken. Having obtained an audience of the superintendent, I told her I had a prospect of getting a new situation where the salary would be double what I now received, and requested she would break the matter for me to Mr. Brocklehurst, or some of the committee, and ascertain whether they would permit me to mention them as references. The next day she laid the affair before Mr. Brocklehurst, who said that Mrs. Reed must be written to, as she was my natural guardian. A note was accordingly addressed to that lady, who returned for answer that I might do as I pleased: she had long relinquished all interference in my affairs. This note went the round of the committee, and at last formal leave was given me to better my condition if I could; and, as I had always conducted myself well at Lowood, a testimonial of character and capacity was furnished me. I accordingly forwarded a copy of this testimonial to Mrs. Fairfax, and got that lady's reply, stating that she was satisfied, and fixing that day fortnight as the period for my assuming the post of governess in her house.

I now busied myself in preparations; the fortnight passed rapidly. I had not a very large wardrobe, though it was adequate to my wants; and the last day sufficed to pack my trunk—the same I had brought with me eight years ago from Gateshead.

The box was corded, the card nailed on. In half an hour the carrier was to call for it to take it to Lowton, whither I myself was to repair at an early hour the next morning to meet the coach. I had brushed my black stuff traveling dress, prepared my bonnet, gloves and muff; and now, having nothing more to do, I sat down and tried to rest. I could not; I was too much excited. A phase of my life was closing tonight, a new one opening tomorrow: impossible to slumber in the interval.

"Miss," said a servant, "a person below wishes to see you."

The carrier, no doubt, I thought, and ran downstairs without inquiry. I was passing the back parlor, when someone ran out crying:

"It's her, I am sure! I could have told her anywhere!"

I saw a woman attired like a well-dressed servant, matronly, yet still young and very good-looking. "Well, who is it?" she asked with a smile. "You've not quite forgotten me, I think, Miss Jane?"

In another second I was embracing her rapturously. "Bessie! Bessie!" whereat she half laughed, half cried, and we both went into the parlor. By the fire stood a little fellow of three years old, in plaid frock and trousers.

"That is my little boy," said Bessie. "I am married to Robert Leaven, the coachman, and I've a little girl besides Bobby there."

"Well, and how do they all get on at Gateshead? Tell me everything about them, Bessie."

"You're not grown so very tall, Miss Jane, nor so very stout," continued Bessie. "Miss Reed is head and shoulders taller than you are; and Miss Georgiana would make two of you in breadth."

"Georgiana is handsome, I suppose, Bessie?"

"Very. She went up to London last winter, and there everybody admired her, and a young lord fell in love with her, but his relations were against the match, and—what do you think?—he and

Miss Georgiana made it up to run away, but they were found out and stopped."

"What of John Reed?"

"Oh, he is not doing so well as his mama could wish. He went to college, and he got—plucked, I think they call it; and then his uncles wanted him to study the law, but he is such a dissipated young man, they will never make much of him, I think."

"And Mrs. Reed?"

"Missis looks stout and well enough in the face, but I think she's not quite easy in her mind. Mr. John's conduct does not please her—he spends a deal of money."

"Did she send you here, Bessie?"

"No, indeed. But I have long wanted to see you, and when I heard that there had been a letter from you, and that you were going to another part of the country, I thought I'd get a look at you before you were quite out of my reach."

"I am afraid you are disappointed in me, Bessie." I said this laughingly; I perceived that Bessie's glance, though it expressed regard, did not denote admiration.

"No, Miss Jane, not exactly. You are genteel enough; you look like a lady, and it is as much as ever I expected of you; you were no beauty as a child. I daresay you are clever, though," continued Bessie. "Can you play on the piano?"

"A little."

There was one in the room; Bessie asked me to sit down and give her a tune. I played a waltz or two, and she was charmed.

"The Miss Reeds could not play as well!" said she exultingly; "and can you draw?"

"That is one of my paintings over the chimneypiece." It was a landscape in watercolors.

"Well, that is beautiful, Miss Jane! It is as fine a picture as any Miss Reed's drawing master could paint. Oh, you will get on whether your relations notice you or not, Miss Jane! There was something I wanted to ask you. Have you ever heard anything from your father's kinfolk, the Eyres?"

"Never in my life."

"Well, you know Missis always said they were poor and quite despicable, but I believe they are as much gentry as the Reeds are; for one day, nearly seven years ago, a Mr. Eyre came to Gateshead and wanted to see you; Missis said you were at school fifty miles off. He seemed so much disappointed, for he could not stay: he was going to a foreign country. He looked quite a gentleman, and I believe he was your father's brother."

"What foreign country was he going to, Bessie?"

"An island thousands of miles off, where they make wine—the butler did tell me—"

"Madeira?" I suggested.

"Yes, that is it."

Bessie and I conversed an hour longer, and then she was obliged to leave me. I saw her again for a few minutes the next morning at Lowton while I was waiting for the coach. We parted finally at the door of the Brocklehurst Arms. There each went her separate way; she set off in the conveyance which was to take her back to Gateshead as I mounted the vehicle which was to bear me to new duties and a new life in the unknown environs of Millcote.

WHEN THE COACH STOPPED at the George Inn at Millcote, at eight that evening, there was no one to meet me. I had no resource but to request to be shown into a private room; and here I waited, sitting near the fire in my cloak and bonnet, while all sorts of doubts and fears troubled my thoughts. It is a very strange sensation to inexperienced youth to feel itself quite alone in the world, cut adrift from every connection, uncertain whether the port to which it is bound can be reached. The charm of adventure sweetens that sensation, the glow of pride warms it; but then the throb of fear disturbs it, and fear with me became predominant, when half an hour elapsed and still I was alone. I bethought myself to ring the bell.

"Is there a place in this neighborhood called Thornfield?" I asked of the waiter who answered the summons.

"Thornfield? I don't know, ma'am; I'll inquire at the bar." He vanished, but reappeared instantly. "Is your name Eyre, miss?"

"Yes."

"Person here waiting for you."

I jumped up, took my muff and umbrella and hastened into the inn passage; a man was standing by the open door, and in the lamplit street I dimly saw a one-horse conveyance. The man hoisted my trunk onto the vehicle, and then I got in; before he shut me up, I asked him how far it was to Thornfield.

"A matter of six miles."

"How long shall we be before we get there?"

"Happen an hour and a half."

He climbed to his own seat outside, and we set off. Our progress was leisurely, and gave me ample time to reflect.

I suppose, thought I, judging from the plainness of the servant and carriage, Mrs. Fairfax is not a very dashing person. So much the better; I never lived among fine people but once, and I was very miserable with them. I wonder if she lives alone except for this little girl, and if she is amiable. Well, I am not bound to stay with her; let the worst come to the worst, I can advertise again.

The roads were heavy, the night misty; my conductor let his horse walk all the way, and the hour and a half extended to two hours. At last he turned in his seat and said:

"You're noan so far fro' Thornfield now."

I looked out; we were passing a church; I saw its low broad tower against the sky. I saw a narrow galaxy of lights too, on a hill-side, marking a village. About ten minutes after, the driver got down and opened a pair of gates; we now slowly ascended a drive, and came upon the long front of a house. Candlelight gleamed from one curtained bow window; all the rest were dark. The car stopped at the front door; it was opened by a maidservant. I alighted and went in.

"Will you walk this way, ma'am," said the girl, and I followed her across a square hall with high doors. She ushered me into a room whose double illumination of fire and candle at first dazzled me; when I could see, however, a cozy and agreeable picture presented itself to my view.

A snug, small room, a round table by a cheerful fire, a high-

backed armchair, wherein sat the neatest imaginable little elderly lady, in widow's cap, black silk gown and snowy muslin apron. She was occupied in knitting, but as I entered, she got up and came forward to meet me.

"How do you do, my dear? I am afraid you have had a tedious ride; you must be cold. Come to the fire."

"Mrs. Fairfax, I suppose?" said I.

"Yes, you are right. Do sit down. Leah, make a little hot negus and cut a sandwich or two; here are the keys of the storeroom." And she produced from her pocket a most housewifely bunch of keys, and delivered them to the servant. "Now then, draw nearer to the fire," she continued to me. "You've brought your luggage with you, haven't you, my dear?"

"Yes, ma'am."

"I'll see it carried into your room," she said, and bustled out.

She treats me like a visitor, thought I. I little expected such a reception; this is not like what I have heard of the treatment of governesses.

She returned, cleared her knitting from the table to make room for the tray which Leah now brought, and then herself handed me the refreshments. I felt rather confused at being the object of so much attention, and that, too, shown by my employer. But as she did not herself seem to consider she was doing anything out of her place, I thought it better to take her civilities quietly.

"Shall I have the pleasure of seeing Miss Fairfax tonight?" I asked, when I had partaken of what she offered me.

"What did you say, my dear? I am a little deaf," returned the good lady, approaching her ear to my mouth. I repeated the question more distinctly. "Miss Fairfax? Oh, you mean Miss Varens? Varens is the name of your pupil."

"Indeed! Then she is not your daughter?"

"No, I have no family."

I should have followed up my first inquiry, but I recollected it was not polite to ask too many questions. Besides, I was sure to hear in time.

"I am so glad," she continued, as she sat down opposite to me, "I am so glad you are come. It will be quite pleasant living here now with a companion. To be sure it is pleasant at any time, for Thornfield is a fine old hall, yet you know in wintertime one feels dreary quite alone. I'm sure last winter (it was a severe one, if you recollect) not a creature but the butcher and postman came to the house from November till February, and I really got quite melancholy. Last spring and summer I got on better; and then, just at the commencement of this autumn, little Adèle came with her nurse. A child makes a house alive all at once; and now you are here I shall be quite gay."

My heart warmed to the worthy lady as I heard her talk; and I drew my chair a little nearer to her, and expressed my sincere wish that she might find my company as agreeable as she anticipated.

"But I'll not keep you sitting up late tonight," said she; "you must feel tired. If you have got your feet well warmed, I'll show you your bedroom. I've had the room next to mine prepared for you; it is only a small apartment, but I thought you would like it better than one of the large front chambers. They are so dreary and solitary."

I thanked her for her considerate choice and, as I really felt fatigued, expressed my readiness to retire. She took her candle, and I followed her upstairs. The steps and banisters were of oak; the staircase window was high and latticed; both it and the long gallery into which the bedroom doors opened looked as if they belonged to a church rather than a house. A very chill and vaultlike air pervaded the stairs and gallery, and I was glad, when finally ushered into my chamber, to find it small and furnished in ordinary modern style.

When Mrs. Fairfax had bidden me a kind good-night, and I had fastened my door, I remembered that I was now at last in safe haven. The impulse of gratitude swelled my heart, and I knelt down at the bedside and offered up thanks where thanks were due, not forgetting, ere I rose, to implore aid on my further path, and the power of meriting the kindness which seemed so frankly offered me.

I slept soon and soundly; when I awoke it was broad day. The chamber looked such a bright little place to me as the sun shone in between the gay blue chintz curtains, showing papered walls and a carpeted floor, so unlike the bare planks and stained plaster of Lowood, that my spirits rose, and I thought that a fairer era of life was beginning for me. I dressed myself with care; obliged to be plain, I was still by nature solicitous to be neat. I sometimes regretted that I was not handsomer; I felt it a misfortune that I was so little, so pale, and had features so irregular.

However, when I had brushed my hair very smooth, put on my black frock and adjusted my clean white tucker, I thought I should do respectably enough to appear before Mrs. Fairfax, and that my new pupil would not at least recoil from me with antipathy.

Traversing the long gallery, I descended to the hall. The hall door stood open; I stepped over the threshold. It was a fine autumn morning; the early sun shone serenely on embrowned groves and still green fields. Advancing onto the lawn, I looked up and surveyed the front of the mansion. It was three stories high, of proportions not vast, though considerable: a gentleman's manor house, not a nobleman's seat. Battlements round the top gave it a picturesque look. Its gray front stood out well from the background of a rookery, whose cawing tenants were now on the wing; they flew over the grounds to alight in a great meadow, where an array of mighty old thorn trees at once explained the mansion's designation. Farther off were hills, not so lofty as those round Lowood, nor so craggy, but yet quiet and lonely hills enough, and seeming to embrace Thornfield with a seclusion I had not expected to find so near the locality of Millcote.

I was yet enjoying the prospect, and thinking what a great place it was for one lonely little dame like Mrs. Fairfax to inhabit, when that lady appeared at the door.

"What, out already?" said she. "I see you are an early riser." I went up to her, and was received with an affable kiss and shake of the hand.

"How do you like Thornfield?" she asked. I told her I liked it very much.

"Yes," she said, "it is a pretty place; but I fear it will be getting out of order, unless Mr. Rochester should take it into his head to visit it rather oftener."

"Mr. Rochester!" I exclaimed. "Who is he?"

"The owner of Thornfield," she responded quietly. "Did you not know he was called Rochester?"

Of course I did not—I had never heard of him; but the old lady seemed to regard his existence as a universally understood fact.

"I thought," I continued, "Thornfield belonged to you."

"To me? Bless you, child! I am only the housekeeper. To be sure, I am distantly related to the Rochesters by the mother's side, or, at least, my husband was. The present Mr. Rochester's mother was a Fairfax and second cousin to my husband, but I never presume on the connection—I consider myself quite in the light of an ordinary housekeeper."

"And the little girl—my pupil?"

"She is Mr. Rochester's ward; he commissioned me to find a governess for her. Here she comes, with her 'bonne,' as she calls her nurse." The enigma then was explained: this affable and kind little widow was a dependent like myself. I did not like her the worse for that; on the contrary, I felt better pleased. The equality between her and me was real; so much the better—my position was all the freer.

As I was meditating on this discovery, a little girl, followed by her attendant, came running up the lawn. She was perhaps seven or eight years old, slightly built, with a pale, small-featured face and a redundancy of hair falling in curls to her waist.

"Good morning, Miss Adèle," said Mrs. Fairfax. "Come and speak to the lady who is to teach you." She approached.

"C'est là ma gouvernante?" said the child, pointing to me and addressing her nurse, who answered:

"Mais oui, certainement."

"Are they foreigners?" I inquired, amazed at hearing French.

"The nurse is a foreigner; Adèle was born on the Continent and, I believe, never left it till six months ago. When she first came here she could speak no English; now she can talk it a little. I don't make out her meaning very well, I daresay."

Fortunately I had had the advantage of being taught French by a French lady at Lowood; I had acquired a certain degree of correctness in the language, and was not likely to be much at a loss with Mademoiselle Adèle. She came and shook hands with me when she heard that I was her governess; and as I led her in to breakfast, I addressed some phrases to her in her own tongue. She replied briefly at first, but after we were seated at the table, and she had examined me some ten minutes with her large hazel eyes, she suddenly commenced chattering fluently.

"Ah," cried she, in French, "you speak my language as well as Mr. Rochester does; I can talk to you as I can to him, and so can Sophie. Sophie is my nurse; she came with me over the sea in a great ship with a chimney that smoked, and I was sick, and so was Sophie, and so was Mr. Rochester. Mademoiselle—what is your name?"

"Eyre—Jane Eyre."

"Aire? Bah! I cannot say it. Well, our ship stopped in the morning, before it was quite daylight, at a great smoky city—not at all like the pretty clean town I came from."

"Can you understand her when she runs on so fast?" asked Mrs. Fairfax.

I understood her very well.

"I wish," continued the good lady, "you would ask her a question or two about her parents: I wonder if she remembers them?"

"Adèle," I inquired, "with whom did you live when you were in that pretty clean town you spoke of?"

"I lived long ago with Mama; but she is gone to the Holy Virgin. Mama used to teach me to dance and sing. A great many gentlemen and ladies came to see Mama, and I used to dance before them, or sit on their knees and sing. Shall I let you hear me sing now?"

She came and placed herself on my knee; then, folding her little hands demurely before her and lifting her eyes to the ceiling, she commenced singing a song from some opera. It was the strain of a forsaken lady bewailing the perfidy of her lover; the subject seemed strangely chosen for an infant singer. She sang it tunefully enough, and with the naïveté of her age. This achieved, she jumped from my knee and said, "Now, Mademoiselle, I will repeat you some poetry." Assuming an attitude, she began "La ligue des rats, fable de La Fontaine." She then declaimed the little piece with a flexibility of voice and an appropriateness of gesture very unusual at her age, and which proved she had been carefully trained.

"Was it your mama who taught you that piece?" I asked.

"Yes. Now shall I dance for you?"

"No, that will do. After your mama went to the Holy Virgin, with whom did you live then?"

"With Madame Frédéric and her husband. I think she is poor, for she had not so fine a house as Mama. Then Mr. Rochester asked me if I would like to go and live with him in England, and I said yes; for I knew Mr. Rochester before I knew Madame Frédéric, and he was always kind to me and gave me pretty dresses and toys. But he has brought me to England, and now he has gone back again himself, and I never see him."

After breakfast, Adèle and I withdrew to the library, which Mr. Rochester had directed should be used as the schoolroom. I found my pupil sufficiently docile, though disinclined to apply: she had not been used to regular occupation of any kind. I felt it would be injudicious to confine her too much at first; so, when I had talked to her a great deal, and got her to learn a little, and when the morning had advanced to noon, I allowed her to return to her nurse. I then proposed to occupy myself till dinner time in drawing some little sketches for her use.

As I was going upstairs to fetch my portfolio and pencils, Mrs. Fairfax called to me: "Your morning school hours are over now, I suppose." She was in a room the folding doors of which stood open; I went in as she addressed me. It was a large, stately apartment, with purple chairs and curtains, a Turkey carpet, walnut-paneled walls, one vast window rich in stained glass, and a lofty ceiling.

"What a beautiful room!" I exclaimed, as I looked round; for I had never before seen any half so imposing.

"Yes; this is the dining room. I have just opened the window, to let in a little air and sunshine, for eveything gets so damp in apartments that are seldom inhabited. The drawing room yonder feels like a vault."

She pointed to an arch hung with a crimson curtain, now looped up. Mounting to it by two steps and looking through, I thought I caught a glimpse of a fairy place, so bright to my novice eyes appeared the view. Yet it was merely a very pretty drawing room, and within it a boudoir, both spread with white carpets, on which seemed laid brilliant garlands of flowers; both ceiled with snowy moldings of white grapes and vine leaves, beneath which glowed in rich contrast crimson couches and ottomans; while the ornaments on the pale Parian mantelpiece were of sparkling Bohemian glass, ruby red.

"In what order you keep these rooms, Mrs. Fairfax!" said I. "No dust, no canvas coverings; except that the air feels chilly, one would think they were inhabited daily."

"Why, Miss Eyre, though Mr. Rochester's visits here are rare, they are always sudden and unexpected; and as I observed that it put him out to find everything swathed up on his arrival, I thought it best to keep the rooms in readiness."

"Is Mr. Rochester an exacting sort of man?"

"Not particularly so; but he has a gentleman's tastes and habits, and he expects to have things managed in conformity to them."

"Do you like him? Is he generally liked?"

"Oh, yes; the family have always been respected here. Almost all the land in this neighborhood, as far as you can see, has belonged to the Rochesters time out of mind."

"Well, but, leaving his land out of the question, do you like him? Is he liked for himself?"

"*I* have no cause to do otherwise than like him; and I believe he is considered a just and liberal landlord by his tenants."

"But has he no peculiarities? What, in short, is his character?"

"Oh, his character is unimpeachable, I suppose. He is rather peculiar, perhaps; he has traveled a great deal and seen a great deal of the world."

"In what way is he peculiar?"

"I don't know—nothing striking, but you feel it when he speaks to you. You cannot be always sure whether he is in jest or earnest, whether he is pleased or the contrary; you don't thoroughly understand him, in short, at least I don't. But it is of no consequence, he is a very good master."

This was all the account I got from Mrs. Fairfax, of her employer and mine. Mr. Rochester was Mr. Rochester in her eyes, a gentleman, a landed proprietor—nothing more. She evidently wondered at my wish to gain a more definite notion of his identity.

When we left the dining room, she proposed to show me over the rest of the house; and I followed her upstairs and downstairs, admiring as I went. The large front chambers I thought especially grand; and some of the third-story rooms, though dark and low, were interesting from their air of antiquity. Furniture from the lower apartments had from time to time been removed here, as fashions changed; and the imperfect light entering by the narrow casements showed bedsteads a hundred years old, chests in oak and walnut with strange carvings of palm branches and cherubs' heads, and venerable chairs, high-backed and narrow.

"Do the servants sleep in these rooms?" I asked.

"No; they occupy a range of smaller apartments to the back; no one ever sleeps up here. One would almost say that, if there were a ghost at Thornfield Hall, this would be its haunt."

"You have no ghost, then?"

"None that I ever heard of," returned Mrs. Fairfax, smiling. "And yet it is said the Rochesters have been rather violent in their time. Perhaps, though, that is the reason they rest tranquilly in their graves now."

"Yes— 'After life's fitful fever they sleep well,'" I muttered. "Where are you going now, Mrs. Fairfax?" for she was moving away.

"Onto the roof; will you come and see the view from thence?" I followed up a very narrow staircase to the attic, and thence by a ladder and through a trapdoor to the roof. I was now on a level with the crow colony, and could see into their nests. Leaning over the battlements and looking far down, I surveyed the grounds laid out like a map: the bright and velvet lawn closely girdling the gray base of the mansion; the field, dotted with its ancient timber; the church at the gates, the road, the tranquil hills, all reposing in the autumn day's sun. No feature in the scene was extraordinary, but all was pleasing. When I turned from it and repassed the trapdoor, I could scarcely see my way down the ladder; the attic seemed black as a vault compared with that sunlit scene of grove, pasture and green hill.

Mrs. Fairfax stayed behind a moment to fasten the trapdoor; I, by dint of groping, proceeded to descend the narrow garret staircase. I lingered in the long passage to which this led, separating the front and back rooms of the third story: narrow, low and dim, with only one little window at the far end, and looking, with its two rows of small black doors all shut, like a corridor in some bluebeard's castle.

While I paced softly on, the last sound I expected to hear in so still a region, a laugh, struck my ear. It was a curious laugh, distinct, formal, mirthless. I stopped. The sound ceased, only for an instant; it began again, louder, till it passed off in a clamorous peal that seemed to wake an echo in every lonely chamber.

"Mrs. Fairfax!" I called out, for I now heard her descending the great stairs. "Did you hear that loud laugh? Who is it?"

"Grace Poole, very likely," she answered.

"Did you hear it?" I again inquired.

"Yes, plainly. I often hear her; she sews in one of these rooms. Sometimes Leah the housemaid is with her; they are frequently noisy together."

The laugh was repeated in its low, syllabic tone, and terminated in an odd murmur.

"Grace!" exclaimèd Mrs. Fairfax.

I really did not expect any Grace to answer; for the laugh was as tragic, as preternatural a laugh as any I ever heard; and, but that it was high noon, and that no circumstance of ghostliness accompanied the curious cachinnation, I should have been superstitiously afraid. However, the event showed me I was a fool for entertaining a sense even of surprise. The door nearest me opened, and a servant came out—a woman of between thirty and forty, a set, square figure, red-haired, and with a hard, plain face. Any apparition less ghostly could scarcely be conceived.

"Too much noise, Grace," said Mrs. Fairfax. "Remember directions!" Grace curtsied silently and went in.

"She is a person we have to sew and assist Leah in her housework," continued the widow; "not altogether unobjectionable in some points, but she does well enough. By-the-bye, how have you got on with your new pupil this morning?"

The conversation, thus turned on Adèle, continued till we reached the light and cheerful region below. There Adèle came running to meet us, and we found dinner ready and waiting.

CHAPTER VI

THE PROMISE OF A SMOOTH career at Thornfield Hall was not belied on a longer acquaintance with the place and its inmates. Mrs. Fairfax turned out to be what she appeared, a placid-tempered, kind-natured woman. My pupil was a lively child, who had been spoiled and indulged, and therefore was sometimes wayward; but as she was committed entirely to my care, and no interference from any quarter ever thwarted my plans for her improvement, she soon became obedient and teachable.

October, November, December passed away. One afternoon in January, Mrs. Fairfax had begged a holiday for Adèle, because she had a cold; and, as Adèle seconded the request with an ardor that reminded me how precious holidays had been to me in my own childhood, I accorded it. It was a fine, calm day, though very cold; I was tired of sitting still; Mrs. Fairfax had written a letter which was waiting to be posted, so I put on my bonnet and cloak and volunteered to carry it to Hay. The distance, two miles, would be a pleasant winter-afternoon walk.

The ground was hard, the air was still, my road was lonely. I walked fast till I got warm, and then I walked slowly to enjoy the hour and situation. It was after three; the pale-beaming sun was gliding low. I was a mile from Thornfield, in a lane noted for wild roses in summer, but whose best winter delight lay in its utter solitude and leafless repose. Far and wide, on each side, there were only fields, where no cattle now browsed; and the little brown birds, which stirred occasionally in the hedge, looked like single russet leaves that had forgotten to drop.

This lane inclined uphill all the way to Hay; having reached the middle, I sat down on a stile. Gathering my mantle about me, I did not feel the cold, though it froze keenly, as was attested by a sheet of ice on the causeway. From my seat I could look down on Thornfield: its woods and dark rookery rose against the west. I lingered till the sun sank crimson behind the trees. I then turned eastward.

On the hilltop above me sat the rising moon; she looked over Hay, which, half lost in trees, sent up a blue smoke from its chimneys; in the absolute hush I could hear plainly its murmurs of life. My ear too felt the flow of currents; in what depths and dales I could not tell, but there were many little hills beyond Hay, and doubtless many becks threading their passes. That evening calm betrayed alike the tinkle of the nearest streams, the sough of the most remote.

A rude noise broke on these fine ripplings and whisperings: a positive tramp, tramp; a metallic clatter, which effaced the soft wave-wanderings. The din was on the causeway; a horse was coming; the windings of the lane yet hid it, but it approached. I was just leaving the stile; yet, as the path was narrow, I sat still to let it go by. In those days I was young, and all sorts of fancies bright and dark tenanted my mind; the memories of nursery stories were there among other rubbish, and as this horse approached through the dusk, I remembered certain of Bessie's tales, wherein figured a North-of-England spirit, called a "Gytrash," which, in the form of horse, mule or large dog, haunted solitary ways, and sometimes came upon belated travelers, as this horse was now coming upon me.

It was very near, but not yet in sight, when, in addition to the tramp, tramp, I heard a rush under the hedge, and close down by the hazel stems glided a great black-and-white dog. It was exactly one mask of Bessie's Gytrash—a lionlike creature with long hair and a huge head. It passed me, however, quietly enough; the horse followed—a tall steed, and on its back a rider. The man, the human being, broke the spell at once. Nothing ever rode the Gytrash; it was always alone. The traveler passed, and I went on. A few steps, and I turned: a sliding sound and an exclamation and a clattering tumble arrested my attention. Man and horse were down; they had slipped on the ice which glazed the causeway. The dog came bounding back, and seeing his master in a predicament, barked till the hills echoed the sound. He snuffed round the prostrate group, and then he ran up to me. I walked to the traveler, by this time struggling himself free of his steed. His efforts were so vigorous, I thought he could not be much hurt; but I asked:

"Are you injured, sir?"

I think he was swearing, but am not certain; however, he was pronouncing some formula which prevented him from replying to me directly. "Can I do anything?" I asked again.

"You must stand on one side," he answered as he rose.

I did; whereupon began a heaving, stamping, clattering process, accompanied by a barking and baying. Finally the horse was

re-established, and the dog was silenced with a "Down, Pilot!"
The traveler now, stooping, felt his foot and leg, as if trying
whether they were sound; apparently something ailed them, for he
limped to the stile whence I had just risen, and sat down.

I was in the mood for being useful, I think, for I now drew near
him again. "If you are hurt, and want help, sir, I can fetch someone
either from Thornfield Hall or from Hay."

"Thank you; I shall do. I have no broken bones—only a
sprain"; and again he stood up and tried his foot, but the result
extorted an involuntary "Ugh!"

Something of daylight still lingered, and the moon was waxing bright; I could see him plainly. His figure was enveloped in a rid-ing cloak, fur-collared; I traced the general points of middle height, and considerable breadth of chest. He had a dark face, with stern features and a heavy brow; he was past youth; perhaps he might be thirty-five. I felt no fear of him, and but little shyness. Had he been a handsome, heroic-looking young gentleman who had smiled and been good-humored to me, I should not have dared to stand thus questioning. But his frown, his roughness set me at my ease: I re-tained my station when he waved to me to go, and announced, "I cannot think of leaving you, sir, in this solitary lane, till I see you are fit to mount your horse."

He looked at me when I said this; he had hardly turned his eyes in my direction before. "I should think you ought to be at home yourself," said he. "Where do you come from?"

"From just below; and I am not at all afraid of being out late when it is moonlight. I will run to Hay for you with pleasure, if you wish it; indeed, I am going there to post a letter."

"You live just below. Do you mean at that house with the battlements?" pointing to Thornfield Hall.

"Yes, sir."

"Whose house is it?"

"Mr. Rochester's."

"Do you know Mr. Rochester?"

"No, I have never seen him."

"You are not a servant at the hall, of course. You are—" He stopped, ran his eye over my dress; he seemed puzzled to decide what I was. I helped him.

"I am the governess."

"Ah, the governess!" he repeated; "deuce take me, if I had not forgotten!" and again my raiment underwent scrutiny. In two minutes he rose from the stile; his face expressed pain when he tried to move. "I cannot commission you to fetch help," he said; "but you may help me a little yourself, if you will be so kind."

"Yes, sir."

"Try to get hold of my horse's bridle and lead him to me. You are not afraid?"

I should have been afraid to touch a horse when alone, but when told to do it, I was disposed to obey. I went up to the tall steed; I endeavored to catch the bridle, but it was a spirited thing and would not let me come near its head; meantime, I was mortally afraid of its trampling forefeet. The traveler laughed. "I see," he said, "the mountain will never be brought to Mohammed, so all you can do is to aid Mohammed to go to the mountain; I must beg of you to come here."

I came. "Excuse me," he continued; "necessity compels me." He laid a heavy hand on my shoulder, and leaning on me with some stress, limped to his horse. Having once caught the bridle, he mastered it directly and sprang to his saddle, grimacing as he made the effort, for it wrenched his sprain.

"Now," said he, "just hand me my whip; it lies there under the hedge."

I sought it and found it.

"Thank you. Now make haste with the letter to Hay, and return as fast as you can."

A touch of a heel made his horse first start and rear, and then bound away; the dog rushed in his traces; all three vanished.

I took up my muff and walked on. The incident had occurred and was gone for me; it was an incident of no moment, yet it marked with change one single hour of a monotonous life. My help had been needed; I had given it, and I was pleased. The new face, too, was like a new picture introduced to the gallery of memory; and it was dissimilar to all the others hanging there: firstly, because it was masculine, and, secondly, because it was dark, strong and stern. I had it still before me when I entered Hay, and slipped the letter into the post office; I saw it as I walked downhill all the way home.

I did not like returning to Thornfield. To pass its threshold was to return to stagnation, to quell wholly the faint excitement wakened by my walk. But when I entered the house the hall was not dark: a warm glow suffused it. This ruddy shine issued from the great dining room, whose two-leaved door stood open and showed a genial fire in the grate. It revealed, too, a group near the mantelpiece. I had scarcely caught it, and scarcely become aware of a cheerful mingling of voices, among which I seemed to distinguish the tones of Adèle, when the door closed.

I hastened to Mrs. Fairfax's room; there was a fire there too, but no candle, and no Mrs. Fairfax. Instead, all alone, sitting upright on the rug, and gazing with gravity at the blaze, was a great black-and-white long-haired dog, just like the Gytrash of the lane. It was so like it that I went forward and said, "Pilot," and the thing got up and came to me and snuffed me. I caressed him, and he wagged his great tail. I rang the bell, for I wanted a candle; and I wanted, too, to get an account of this visitant. Leah entered.

"What dog is this?"

"He came with master."

"With whom?"

"With Mr. Rochester—he is just arrived. Mrs. Fairfax and Miss Adèle are with him in the dining room, and John is gone for a surgeon, for master has had an accident. His horse fell and his ankle is sprained."

"Did the horse fall in Hay Lane?"

"Yes; it slipped on some ice."

"Ah! Bring me a candle, will you, Leah?"

Leah brought it; then I went upstairs to take off my things.

MR. ROCHESTER, by the surgeon's orders, went to bed early that night; nor did he rise soon next morning. When he did come down, it was to attend to business. His agent and some of his tenants were arrived and waiting to speak with him.

Adèle and I had now to vacate the library: it would be in daily requisition as a reception room for callers. A fire was lit in an apartment upstairs, and there I carried our books. I soon discerned that Thornfield Hall was a changed place: it echoed every hour or two to a knock at the door; steps traversed the hall, and new voices spoke; a rill from the outer world was flowing through it; it had a master. For my part, I liked it better.

Adèle was not easy to teach that day; she kept running to the door and looking over the banisters to see if she could get a glimpse of Mr. Rochester. Then, when I made her sit still, she talked incessantly of her "ami, Monsieur Edouard Fairfax de Rochester," and of what presents he might have brought her. She and I dined as usual in Mrs. Fairfax's parlor; the afternoon was snowy, and we passed it in the schoolroom. At dark I allowed Adèle to run downstairs, for, from the comparative silence below, I conjectured that Mr. Rochester was now at liberty. Left alone at the fireside, I was tracing a view in the clear embers when Mrs. Fairfax came in.

"Mr. Rochester would be glad if you and your pupil would take tea with him in the drawing room," said she; "he has been so much engaged all day that he could not ask to see you before."

"When is his teatime?" I inquired.

"At six o'clock. You had better change your frock now; I will go with you and fasten it. Here is a candle."

I repaired to my room, and, with Mrs. Fairfax's aid, replaced my black stuff dress by one of green silk; the best and only additional one I had except one of light gray, which, in my Lowood notions, I thought too fine to be worn except on first-rate occasions. "You want a brooch," said Mrs. Fairfax. I had a little pearl ornament which Miss Temple had given me as a parting keepsake. I put it on, and then we went downstairs. Unused as I was to strangers, it was rather a trial to appear thus formally summoned in Mr. Rochester's presence. I let Mrs. Fairfax precede me into the drawing room.

Candles stood lighted on the table and the mantelpiece; basking in the light and heat of a superb fire lay Pilot. Adèle knelt near him. Half reclined on a couch appeared Mr. Rochester, his foot supported by the cushion; he was looking at Adèle and the dog; the fire shone full on his face. I knew my traveler with his broad and jetty eyebrows; I recognized his decisive nose, more remarkable for character than beauty; his grim mouth, chin and jaw.

Mr. Rochester must have been aware of the entrance of Mrs. Fairfax and myself, but it appeared he was not in the mood to notice us, for he never lifted his head as we approached.

"Here is Miss Eyre, sir," said Mrs. Fairfax.

He bowed stiffly, still not taking his eyes from the dog and child.

"Let Miss Eyre be seated," said he; and there was something in the impatient yet formal tone which seemed to express, What the deuce is it to me whether Miss Eyre be there or not?

I sat down quite disembarrassed. A reception of finished politeness would probably have confused me: I could not have repaid it by grace and elegance on my part. Besides, the eccentricity of the proceeding was piquant: I felt interested to see how he would go on.

He went on as a statue would, that is, he neither spoke nor moved. Mrs. Fairfax seemed to think it necessary that someone should be amiable, and she began to talk. Kindly as usual and, as usual, rather trite, she condoled with him on the pressure of business he had had all day; on the annoyance the sprain must be to him; then she commended his patience and perseverance.

"Madam, I should like some tea," was the sole rejoinder she got. She hastened to ring the bell. When the tray came, Adèle and I went to the table, but the master did not leave his couch.

"Will you hand Mr. Rochester's cup?" said Mrs. Fairfax to me. "Adèle might perhaps spill it."

I did as requested. As he took the cup from my hand, Adèle, thinking the moment propitious for making a request in my favor, cried out: "N'est-ce pas, monsieur, qu'il y a un cadeau pour Mademoiselle Eyre dans votre petit coffre?"

"Who talks of *cadeaux*?" said he, gruffly. "Did you expect a present, Miss Eyre? Are you fond of presents?" and he searched my face with eyes that I saw were dark, irate and piercing.

"I hardly know, sir; I have little experience of them. They are generally thought pleasant things."

"Miss Eyre, you are not so unsophisticated as Adèle. She demands a 'cadeau,' clamorously, the moment she sees me. You beat about the bush."

"Because I have less confidence in my deserts than Adèle has. She can prefer the claim of old acquaintance; but if I had to make out a case I should be puzzled, since I have done nothing to entitle me to an acknowledgment."

"Oh, don't fall back on overmodesty! I have examined Adèle,

and find you have taken great pains with her. In a short time she has made much improvement."

"Sir, you have now given me my 'cadeau'; I am obliged to you. It is the meed teachers most covet—praise of their pupils' progress."

"Humph!" said Mr. Rochester, and he took his tea in silence. Then when the tray was taken away, and Mrs. Fairfax had settled into a corner with her knitting, he spoke again:

"Come to the fire," he said. Adèle and I obeyed; Adèle wanted to take a seat on my knee, but she was ordered to amuse herself with Pilot.

"You have been resident in my house three months?"

"Yes, sir."

"And you come from—?"

"From Lowood school, in ——shire."

"Ah, a charitable concern! How long were you there?"

"Eight years."

"Eight years! You must be tenacious of life. I thought half the time in such a place would have done up any constitution! No wonder you have rather the look of another world. Who are your parents?"

"I have none."

"Nor ever had, I suppose. Do you remember them?"

"No."

"I thought not. And so you were waiting for your people when you sat on that stile?"

"For whom, sir?"

"For the men in green. It was a proper moonlight evening for them. Did I break through one of your rings, that you spread that damned ice on the causeway?"

I shook my head. "The men in green all forsook England a hundred years ago," said I, speaking as seriously as he had done. "And not even in Hay Lane could you find a trace of them. I don't think either summer or harvest, or winter moon, will ever shine on their revels more."

Mrs. Fairfax had dropped her knitting, and, with raised eyebrows, seemed wondering what sort of talk this was.

"Well," resumed Mr. Rochester, "if you disown parents, you must have some sort of kinsfolk: uncles and aunts?"

"No; none that I ever saw."

"Who recommended you to come here?"

"I advertised, and Mrs. Fairfax answered my advertisement."

"Yes," said the good lady, who now knew what ground we were upon, "and I am daily thankful for the choice Providence led me to make. Miss Eyre has been an invaluable companion to me, and a kind and careful teacher to Adèle."

"Don't trouble yourself to give her a character," returned Mr. Rochester. "I shall judge for myself. She began by felling my horse."

"Sir?" said Mrs. Fairfax.

"I have to thank her for this sprain."

The widow looked bewildered.

"Miss Eyre, have you ever lived in a town?"

"No, sir."

"Have you seen much society?"

"None but the pupils and teachers of Lowood, and now the inmates of Thornfield."

"And what did you learn at Lowood? Can you play?"

"A little."

"Of course; that is the established answer. Go into the library—I mean, if you please. Excuse my tone of command; I am used to say 'Do this,' and it is done. I cannot alter my customary habits for one new inmate. Go, then, into the library; sit down to the piano, and play a tune." I departed, obeying his directions. "Enough!" he called out in a few minutes. "You play a *little*, I see, like any other English schoolgirl."

I closed the piano, and returned. Mr. Rochester continued:

"Adèle showed me some sketches this morning, which she said were yours. I don't know whether they were entirely of your doing; probably a master aided you?"

"No, indeed!" I interjected.

"Ah, that pricks pride. Well, fetch me your portfolio, if you can vouch for its contents being original."

I brought the portfolio from the library, and Mr. Rochester deliberately scrutinized each sketch and painting. Three he laid aside; the others he swept from him.

"Take them off to the other table, Mrs. Fairfax," said he, "and look at them with Adèle; you"—glancing at me—"resume your seat, and answer my questions. I perceive these pictures were done by one hand; was that hand yours?"

"Yes."

"Where did you get your copies?"

"Out of my head."

"That head I see now on your shoulders?"

"Yes, sir."

"Has it other furniture of the same kind within?"

"I should think it may have; I should hope—better."

He spread the pictures before him, and again surveyed them alternately. All three were watercolors. The first represented clouds low and livid, rolling over a swollen sea; one gleam of light lifted into relief a half-submerged mast on which sat a cormorant, dark and large, with wings flecked with foam; its beak held a bracelet set with brilliant gems; and sinking below the bird, a drowned corpse glanced through the green water.

The second picture, a vision of the Evening Star, contained for foreground only the dim peak of a hill. Rising into the sky was a woman's head portrayed in tints as dusk and soft as I could combine, against a sky dark blue as at twilight; and her dim forehead was crowned with a star.

The third showed an iceberg piercing a winter sky; northern lights reared their lances, close-serried, along the horizon; and throwing these into distance, rose, in the foreground, a head, a colossal head, above whose temples gleamed a ring of white flame, "The likeness of a Kingly Crown."

"Were you happy when you painted these pictures?" asked Mr. Rochester, presently.

"I was absorbed, sir. Yes, I was happy. To paint them was to enjoy keen pleasure."

"You felt satisfied with the result of your labors?"

"Far from it. In each case I had imagined something which I was powerless to realize."

"Not quite. You have secured the shadow of your thought. Yet the drawings are, for a schoolgirl, peculiar. And who taught you to paint wind? There is a high gale in that sky, and on this hilltop. There, put the drawings away!"

I had scarce tied the strings of the portfolio, when, looking at his watch, he said abruptly, "It is nine o'clock. What are you about, Miss Eyre, to let Adèle sit up so long? Take her to bed."

Adèle went to kiss him before quitting the room; he endured the caress, but scarcely seemed to relish it.

"I wish you all good-night, now," said he, making a movement of the hand towards the door, in token that he was tired of our company, and wished to dismiss us. We curtsied to him, received a frigid bow in return, and so withdrew.

"You said Mr. Rochester was not strikingly peculiar, Mrs. Fairfax," I observed, when I rejoined her in her room, after putting Adèle to bed.

"Well, is he?"

"I think so; he is very changeful and abrupt."

"True. No doubt he may appear so to a stranger, but I am so accustomed to his manner I never think of it; and then, if he has peculiarities of temper, allowance should be made."

"Why?"

"Partly because it is his nature, and, partly, he has painful thoughts, no doubt, to harass him."

"What about?"

"Family troubles, for one thing."

"But he has no family."

"Not now, but he has had. He lost his elder brother a few years since."

"His *elder* brother?"

"Yes. The present Mr. Rochester has not been very long in possession of the property; only about nine years."

"Nine years is a tolerable time. Was he so fond of his brother as to be still inconsolable for his loss?"

"Why, no—perhaps not. I believe there were some misunderstandings between them. Mr. Rowland Rochester was not quite just to Mr. Edward; and, perhaps, he prejudiced his father against him. Mr. Edward is not very forgiving: he broke with his family, and now for many years he has led an unsettled kind of life. I don't think he has ever been resident at Thornfield for a fortnight together, since the death of his brother left him master of the estate; and, indeed, no wonder he shuns the old place."

"Why should he shun it?"

"Perhaps he thinks it gloomy."

The answer was evasive—I should have liked something clearer; but Mrs. Fairfax either could not, or would not, give me more explicit information of the origin and nature of Mr. Rochester's trials. It was evident, indeed, that she wished me to drop the subject, which I did accordingly.

For several subsequent days I saw little of Mr. Rochester. In the mornings he seemed much engaged with business, and, in the afternoon, gentlemen from Millcote or the neighborhood called, and sometimes stayed to dine. When his sprain was well enough he rode out, probably to return these visits, as he generally did not come back till late at night.

Then, however, came a change. Business evidently done, he seemed to have more time, and in the evenings he frequently sent for Adèle, Mrs. Fairfax and myself. We discussed a variety of subjects, and I came to feel as if I knew him rather better, with all his changes of mood.

When he met me unexpectedly now, in the hallway or on the grounds, the encounter seemed welcome to him; he had always a word and sometimes a smile for me; when summoned by formal invitation to his presence, I was honored by a cordiality of reception that made me feel I really possessed the power to amuse him, and that these evening conferences were sought very much for his pleasure. I, indeed, talked comparatively little; but I heard him talk with relish. It was his nature to be communicative: he liked to open, to a mind unacquainted with the world, glimpses of its scenes and ways; and I had a keen delight in receiving the new ideas he offered. The ease of his manner, too, freed me from re-straint: the friendly frankness with which he treated me drew me to him. He was imperious sometimes still; but now I did not mind that: I saw it was his way. So happy, so gratified did I become with this new interest added to life that I ceased to pine after kindred. The blanks of my existence seemed filled up; my bodily health improved.

One afternoon some weeks after his return, he chanced to meet Adèle and me in the grounds; and while she played with Pilot and her shuttlecock, he asked me to walk up and down a long beech avenue within sight of her.

He had once promised me an explanation of the circumstances of Adèle's being his ward, and he now gave it to me, telling me that she was the daughter of a French opera dancer, Céline Varens. Towards Céline Varens he had once cherished what he called a "grande passion." This passion Céline had professed to return with even superior ardor. He thought himself her idol; ugly as he was, he believed, as he said, that she preferred his "taille d'athlète" to the elegance of the Apollo Belvedere.

Here ensued a pause, filled up by the producing and lighting of a cigar; having placed it to his lips and breathed a trail of Havana incense on the freezing and sunless air, he went on:

"After some time, however, Céline chose a new companion, a brainless and vicious youth whom I despised; and my love for her sank as under an extinguisher. Some years after I had broken with her, she abandoned her child and ran away to Italy with a musician or singer. I acknowledged no natural claim on Adèle's part to be supported by me; nor do I now, for I am not her father; but hearing that she was quite destitute, I took the poor thing out of the slime and mud of Paris, and transplanted it here, to grow up clean in the wholesome soil of an English country garden. Mrs. Fairfax found you to train it; but now you know that it is the illegitimate offspring of a French opera girl, you will perhaps think differently of your post and protegée; you will be coming to me someday with notice that you have found another place—that you beg me to look out for a new governess, etc.—eh?"

"No. Adèle is not answerable for either her mother's faults or yours; I have a regard for her, and now that I know she is, in a sense, parentless, I shall cling closer to her than before. How could I possibly prefer the spoiled pet of a wealthy family, who would hate her governess as a nuisance, to a lonely little orphan, who leans towards her as a friend?"

"Oh, that is the light in which you view it! Well, I must go in now; and you too. It darkens."

But I stayed out a few minutes longer with Adèle and Pilot—ran a race with her, and played a game of battledore and shuttlecock. When we went in and I had removed her bonnet and coat, I took her on my knee; kept her there an hour, allowing her to prattle as she liked, not rebuking even some little freedoms and trivialities into which she was apt to stray when much noticed, and which betrayed in her a superficiality of character, inherited probably from her mother. Still, she had her merits; and I was disposed to appreciate to the utmost all that was good in her.

It was not till after I had withdrawn to my own chamber for the night that I steadily reviewed the tale Mr. Rochester had told me, and considered anew his manner to myself. The confidence he had thought fit to repose in me seemed a tribute to my discretion; I regarded and accepted it as such.

I had once thought Mr. Rochester ugly; and was he now ugly in my eyes? No, reader; gratitude, and many associations, all pleasurable and genial, made his face the object I now best liked to see; his presence in a room was more cheering than the brightest fire. Yet I had not forgotten his faults; he was proud, sardonic, harsh to inferiority of every description. In my secret soul I knew that his great kindness to me was balanced by unjust severity to many others. He was moody, too; I more than once, when sent for to read to him, found him sitting in his library alone, with his head bent on his folded arms; and, when he looked up, a morose scowl blackened his features. But I believed that his moodiness and his former faults of morality had their source in some cruel cross of fate. I thought there were excellent materials in him, though for the present they hung together somewhat spoiled and tangled. I grieved for his grief, whatever that was, and would have given much to assuage it.

Though I had now extinguished my candle and was laid down in bed, I could not sleep for thinking of Mr. Rochester; for one thing I was wondering why he did not seem to be more happy at Thornfield. What alienates him from the house? I asked myself. Will he leave it again soon? Mrs. Fairfax said he seldom stayed here longer than a fortnight; and he has now been resident eight weeks. If he does go, the change will be doleful!

I hardly knew whether I had slept or not after this musing; at any rate, I started wide awake on hearing a vague murmur, peculiar and lugubrious, which sounded, I thought, just above me. I wished I had kept my candle burning: the night was drearily dark. I sat up in bed, listening. The sound was hushed.

I tried again to sleep; but my heart beat anxiously. The clock, far down in the hall, struck two. Just then it seemed my chamber door was touched, as if fingers had swept the panels in groping a way along the dark gallery outside. I said, "Who is there?" Nothing answered. I was chilled with fear.

All at once I remembered that it might be Pilot, who not unfrequently found his way up to the threshold of Mr. Rochester's chamber. The idea calmed me somewhat: I lay down. Silence composes the nerves; and as an unbroken hush now reigned through the whole house, I began to feel the return of slumber. But it was not fated that I should sleep that night. A dream had scarcely approached my ear, when it fled affrighted, scared by a marrow-freezing incident.

This was a demoniac laugh—low, suppressed and deep—uttered, as it seemed, at the very keyhole of my chamber door. The head of my bed was near the door, and I thought at first the goblin laughter stood at my bedside—or rather, crouched by my pillow; but I rose, looked round, and could see nothing; while, as I still gazed, the unnatural sound was reiterated, and I knew it came from behind the panels. My first impulse was to rise and fasten the bolt; my next, again to cry out, "Who is there?"

Something gurgled and moaned. Ere long, steps retreated up

the gallery towards the third-story staircase; I heard a door open and close, and all was still.

Was that Grace Poole? And is she possessed with a devil? thought I. Impossible now to remain longer by myself: I must go to Mrs. Fairfax. I hurried on my frock and a shawl; I opened the door with a trembling hand. There was a candle burning just outside, left on the matting in the gallery. I was surprised at this; but still more was I amazed to perceive the air quite dim, as if filled with smoke; I became further aware of a strong smell of burning.

Something creaked: it was a door ajar, and that door was Mr. Rochester's, and the smoke rushed in a cloud from thence. In an instant, I was within the chamber. Tongues of flame darted round the bed—the curtains were on fire. In the midst of blaze and vapor, Mr. Rochester lay stretched motionless, in deep sleep.

"Wake! Wake!" I cried. I shook him, but the smoke had stupefied him. Not a moment could be lost: I rushed to his basin and ewer; fortunately both were filled with water. I heaved them up, deluged the bed and its occupant, flew back to my own room, brought my own water jug, baptized the couch afresh, and, by God's aid, succeeded in extinguishing the flames which were devouring it.

The hiss of the quenched element, the breakage of a pitcher which I had flung from my hand when I had emptied it, and, above all, the splash of the shower bath I had liberally bestowed, roused Mr. Rochester at last.

"Is there a flood?" he cried out in the dark.

"No, sir," I answered; "but there has been a fire. Get up, do, you are quenched now. I will fetch you a candle."

"In the name of all the elves in Christendom, is that Jane Eyre?" he demanded. "What have you done with me, witch, sorceress?"

"I will fetch you a candle, sir, and, in Heaven's name, get up. Somebody has plotted something; you cannot too soon find out who and what it is."

"There—I am up now; but at your peril you fetch a candle yet: wait two minutes till I get into some dry garments, if any dry there be—yes, here is my dressing gown. Now run!"

I did run; I brought the candle which still remained in the gallery. He took it, held it up, and surveyed the bed, blackened and scorched, the sheets drenched, the carpet swimming in water.

"What is it? And who did it?" he asked.

I briefly related to him what had transpired. He listened very gravely. His face, as I went on, expressed more concern than astonishment; he did not speak when I had concluded.

"Shall I call Mrs. Fairfax?" I asked.

"Mrs. Fairfax? No; what the deuce can she do? Let her sleep unmolested."

"Then I will fetch Leah, and wake John and his wife."

"Not at all; just be still. You have a shawl on? If you are not warm enough, you may take my cloak yonder; wrap it about you, and sit in the armchair. I am going to leave you a few minutes. I shall take the candle. Remain where you are till I return; be as still as a mouse. I must pay a visit to the third story. Don't move, remember, or call anyone."

He went and I watched the light withdraw. He passed up the

gallery very softly, and the last ray vanished. I was left in total darkness while a very long time elapsed. I grew weary. It was cold, in spite of the cloak; and then I did not see the use of staying, as I was not to rouse the house. I was on the point of disobeying Mr. Rochester's orders, when the light once more gleamed dimly on the gallery wall, and I heard his unshod feet tread the matting. He re-entered, pale and very gloomy. "I have found it all out," said he, setting his candle down; "it is as I thought."

"How, sir?"

He made no reply, but stood with his arms folded, looking on the ground. At the end of a few minutes, he inquired in a peculiar tone, "I forget whether you said you saw anything when you opened your chamber door."

"No, sir, only the candlestick on the ground."

"But you heard an odd laugh?"

"Yes, sir; there is a woman who sews here, called Grace Poole— she laughs in that way. She is a singular person."

"Just so. Grace Poole—you have guessed it. She is, as you say, singular—very. I am glad that you are the only person, besides myself, acquainted with the precise details of tonight's incident. Say nothing about it: I will account for this state of affairs [pointing to the bed]; and now return to your own room. I shall do very well on the sofa in the library for the rest of the night. It is near four; in two hours the servants will be up."

"Good night, then, sir," said I, departing.

He seemed surprised—inconsistently, as he had just told me to go. "What!" he exclaimed. "Are you quitting me already, and in that way?"

"You said I might go, sir."

"But not without a word or two of acknowledgment and good-will. Why, you have saved my life! At least shake hands."

He held out his hand; I gave him mine. He took it first in one, then in both his own.

"You have saved my life. I have a pleasure in owing you so immense a debt. Nothing else that has being would have been tolerable to me in the character of creditor for such an obligation.

But you—it is different; I feel your benefits no burden, Jane."

He paused, gazed at me; words almost visible trembled on his lips, but his voice was checked.

"Good night again, sir. There is no debt, benefit, burden, obligation, in the case."

"I knew," he continued, "you would do me good in some way, at some time—I saw it in your eyes when I first beheld you: their expression and smile did not"—again he stopped—"did not"—he proceeded hastily—"strike delight to my very inmost heart so for nothing. My cherished preserver, good night!"

Strange energy was in his voice, strange fire in his look.

"I am glad I happened to be awake," I said; and then I was going.

"What! You *will* go?"

"I am cold, sir."

"Cold? Yes—and standing in a pool! Go then, Jane; go!" But he still retained my hand, and I could not free it. I bethought myself of an expedient.

"I think I hear Mrs. Fairfax move, sir," said I.

"Well, leave me." He relaxed his fingers, and I was gone.

I regained my couch, but never thought of sleep. Till morning dawned I was tossed on a buoyant but unquiet sea, where billows of trouble rolled under surges of joy. Too feverish to rest, I rose as soon as day dawned.

I BOTH WISHED AND FEARED to see Mr. Rochester: I wanted to hear his voice again, yet feared to meet his eye. During the early part of the morning, I momentarily expected that he might come to the schoolroom.

But nothing happened to interrupt the quiet course of Adèle's studies; only, soon after breakfast, I heard some bustle and exclamations in the neighborhood of Mr. Rochester's chamber.

To much confabulation succeeded a sound of scrubbing and setting to rights; and when I passed the room, in going downstairs to dinner, I saw through the open door that all was again restored to order; only the bed was stripped of its hangings. Leah stood up in the window seat, rubbing the panes of glass dimmed with smoke. I was about to address her, but, on advancing, I saw a second person in the chamber—no other than Grace Poole.

There she sat, staid and taciturn-looking, as usual. She was sewing rings to new curtains, work in which her whole thoughts seemed absorbed. In her commonplace features was nothing of the desperation one would have expected to see marking the countenance of a woman who had attempted murder. I was amazed—confounded. She looked up while I still gazed at her; no increase or failure of color betrayed emotion or consciousness of guilt. She said, "Good morning, Miss," in her brief manner, and taking up another ring, went on with her sewing.

I will put her to some test, thought I; such absolute impenetrability is past comprehension.

"Good morning, Grace," I said. "Has anything happened here? I thought I heard the servants all talking together a while ago."

"Only master had been reading in his bed last night; he fell asleep with his candle lit, and the curtains got on fire; but, fortunately, he awoke, and contrived to quench the flame with water."

"A strange affair!" I said; then, looking at her fixedly, "Did Mr. Rochester wake nobody? Did no one hear him move?"

She again raised her eyes to me; and this time she seemed to examine me warily; then she answered, "The servants sleep so far off, you know, Miss, they would not be likely to hear. Mrs. Fairfax's room and yours are the nearest; but Mrs. Fairfax said she heard nothing." She paused, and then added, in a significant tone, "But you, Miss, perhaps you heard a noise?"

"I did," said I, dropping my voice, so that Leah could not hear me, "and at first I thought it was Pilot; but Pilot cannot laugh, and I am certain I heard a laugh, and a strange one."

She took a new needleful of thread, waxed it, threaded her needle with a steady hand, and then observed, with perfect composure, "It is hardly likely master would laugh, Miss, when he was in such danger; you must have been dreaming."

"I was not dreaming," I said, with warmth, for her coolness provoked me.

"You did not think of opening your door and looking out into the gallery?" she further asked.

She appeared to be cross-questioning me, attempting to draw from me information; I thought it advisable to be on my guard.

"On the contrary," said I, "I bolted my door."

"Then you are not in the habit of bolting your door every night before you get into bed?"

I replied sharply, "Hitherto I have often omitted to fasten the bolt. In future" (and I laid marked stress on the words) "I shall take good care to make all secure before I lie down."

"It will be wise so to do," was her answer. "This neighborhood is quiet, and I never heard of the hall being attempted by robbers; but there are hundreds of pounds' worth of plate in the plate closet, as is well known. And you see, for such a large house, there are very few servants, because master has never lived here much. I always think it best to err on the safe side; it is as well to have a drawn bolt between one and any mischief that may be about." And here she closed her harangue, uttered with the demureness of a Quakeress.

I hardly heard Mrs. Fairfax's account of the curtain conflagration during dinner, so much was I occupied in puzzling my brains over the enigma of Grace Poole, in pondering the problem of her position at Thornfield, and in questioning why she had not been given into custody that morning, or, at the very least, dismissed from her master's service. He had almost as much as declared his conviction of her criminality last night; what mysterious cause withheld him from accusing her? Why had he enjoined me, too, to secrecy? It was strange: a bold, vindictive and haughty gentleman seemed somehow in the power of one of the meanest of his dependents; so much in her power that even when she lifted her hand against his life he dared not openly charge her with the attempt, much less punish her for it.

Had Grace been young and handsome, I should have been tempted to think that tenderer feelings than prudence or fear influenced Mr. Rochester in her behalf; but, hard-favored and matronly as she was, the idea could not be admitted. Yet, said the secret voice that talks to us in our hearts, *you* are not beautiful either, and perhaps Mr. Rochester approves you; at any rate, you have often felt as if he did; and last night—remember his words; remember his look; remember his voice!

I was now in the schoolroom; Adèle was drawing. Evening approaches, I said to myself as I looked towards the window. I have never heard Mr. Rochester's voice or step in the house today; but surely I shall see him before night. I feared the meeting in the morning; now I desire it, because expectation has been so long baffled that it is grown impatient.

When dusk actually closed, and when Adèle left me to go and play in the nursery with Sophie, I did most keenly desire it. I fancied sometimes I heard Mr. Rochester's tread, and I turned to the door, expecting it to open and admit him. The door remained shut; darkness only came in through the window.

A tread creaked on the stairs at last; Leah made her appearance, but it was only to intimate that tea was ready in Mrs. Fairfax's room. Thither I repaired, glad at least to go downstairs; for that brought me, I imagined, nearer to Mr. Rochester's presence.

"You must want your tea," said the good lady; "you ate so little at dinner. I am afraid," she continued, "you are not well today: you look flushed and feverish."

"Oh, quite well! I never felt better."

"Then you must prove it by evincing a good appetite; will you fill the teapot while I knit off this needle?" Having completed her task, she rose to draw down the blind; dusk was now fast deepening into total obscurity. "It is fair tonight," said she, as she looked through the panes; "Mr. Rochester has, on the whole, had a favorable day for his journey."

"Journey! Is Mr. Rochester gone somewhere?"

"Oh, he set off the moment he had breakfasted! He is gone to the Leas, Mr. Eshton's place, ten miles on the other side of Millcote. I believe there is quite a party assembled there."

"Do you expect him back tonight?"

"No—nor tomorrow either; I should think he is very likely to stay a week or more. When these fine, fashionable people get together, they are in no hurry to separate. And Mr. Rochester, I believe, is a general favorite in society; the ladies are very fond of him, though you would not think his appearance calculated to recommend him particularly in their eyes."

"Are there ladies at the Leas?"

"There are Mrs. Eshton and her three daughters—very elegant young ladies; and there are the Honorable Blanche and Mary Ingram—most beautiful women, I suppose. Indeed, I have seen Blanche, six or seven years since, when she was eighteen; she came here to a Christmas ball, and was the belle of the evening."

"What was she like?"

"Tall, fine bust, sloping shoulders; long, graceful neck; raven-black hair; eyes large and black, and as brilliant as her jewels. She was greatly admired not only for her beauty but for her accomplishments. She sang; she and Mr. Rochester sang a duet."

"Mr. Rochester? I was not aware he could sing."

"Oh, he has a fine bass voice, and an excellent taste for music."

"And this beautiful and accomplished lady is not yet married?"

"It appears not; I fancy neither she nor her sister have very large fortunes."

"But I wonder no wealthy gentleman has taken a fancy to her: Mr. Rochester, for instance. He is rich, is he not?"

"Oh, yes! But you see there is a considerable difference in age: Mr. Rochester is near forty; she is but twenty-five."

"What of that? More unequal matches are made every day."

"True, yet I should scarcely fancy Mr. Rochester would entertain an idea of the sort. But you eat nothing: you have scarcely tasted since you began tea."

When once more alone, I reviewed the information I had got; looked into my heart, examined its thoughts and feelings, and endeavored to bring back with a strict hand such as had been straying through imagination's boundless waste, into the safe fold of common sense. Arraigned at my own bar, Memory having given her evidence of the hopes, wishes, sentiments I had been cherishing since last night; and Reason having come forward, I pronounced judgment to this effect:

"*You*," I said, "a favorite with Mr. Rochester? *You* gifted with the power of pleasing him? *You* of importance to him in any way? Go! Your folly sickens me. And you have derived pleasure from occasional tokens of preference shown by a gentleman of family and a man of the world, to a dependent and a novice. How dared you? Poor stupid dupe! Could not even self-interest make you wiser? It does good to no woman to be flattered by her superior, who cannot possibly intend to marry her; and it is madness in any woman to let a secret love kindle within her, which, if unreturned and unknown, must devour the life that feeds it."

Thus I forced my feelings to submit; and ere long, I had reason to congratulate myself on having tried this course of discipline. Thanks to it, I was able to meet subsequent occurrences with a decent calm, which, had they found me unprepared, I should probably have been unequal to maintain, even externally.

CHAPTER VII

A WEEK PASSED, and no news arrived of Mr. Rochester; ten days, and still he did not come. Mrs. Fairfax said she should not be surprised if he were to go straight from the Leas to London, and thence to the Continent; he had not infrequently quitted Thornfield in a manner quite as abrupt and unexpected. When I heard this I was beginning to feel a strange chill at the heart. I was actually permitting myself to experience a sickening sense of disappointment; but rallying my wits, and recollecting my principles, I at once called my sensations to order.

So I went on with my day's business tranquilly; but ever and anon vague suggestions kept wandering across my brain of reasons why I should quit Thornfield, and I kept involuntarily pondering conjectures about new situations. These thoughts I did not think it necessary to check; they might germinate and bear fruit if they could.

Mr. Rochester had been absent upwards of a fortnight, when the post brought Mrs. Fairfax a letter.

"It is from the master," said she. "Now I suppose we shall know whether we are to expect his return or not."

And while she perused the document, I went on taking my coffee (we were at breakfast); it was hot, and I attributed to that circumstance a fiery glow which rose to my face.

"Well—I sometimes think we are too quiet; but we run a chance of being busy enough now, for a little while at least," said Mrs. Fairfax, still holding the note before her spectacles.

I tied the string of Adèle's pinafore, which happened to be loose; having helped her also to another bun and refilled her mug with milk, I said, nonchalantly:

"Mr. Rochester is not likely to return soon, I suppose?"

"Indeed, he is—in three days, he says; that will be next Thursday, and not alone either. I don't know how many of the fine people at the Leas are coming with him: he sends directions for all the best bedrooms to be prepared; and I am to get more kitchen hands; and the ladies will bring their maids and the gentlemen their valets, so we shall have a full house of it." And Mrs. Fairfax hastened away to commence operations.

The three days were, as she had foretold, busy enough. I had thought all the rooms at Thornfield beautifully clean, but it appears I was mistaken. Such scrubbing, such brushing, such washing of paint and beating of carpets, such polishing of mirrors, such airing of sheets and beds, I never beheld, either before or since. Adèle ran wild in the midst of it: the prospect of company threw her into ecstasies. She would have Sophie look over all her "toilettes," as she called frocks, to furbish up any that were "passées," and to air and arrange the new.

The party were expected to arrive on Thursday afternoon, in time for dinner at six. During the intervening period I believe I was as active and gay as anybody. Still, now and then, I was, in spite of myself, thrown back on the region of dark conjectures. This was when I chanced to see the third-story staircase door (which of late had always been kept locked) open slowly, and give passage to the form of Grace Poole, in prim cap and white apron; when I watched her glide along the gallery, her quiet tread muffled in a list slipper. She would thus descend to the kitchen once a day, eat her dinner, and go back, carrying her pot of porter with her, for her private solace in her own gloomy, upper haunt. Only one hour in the twenty-four did she pass with her fellow servants below; all the rest of her time was spent in some low-ceiled, oaken chamber of the third story.

The strangest thing of all was that not a soul in the house, except me, seemed to marvel at her habits; no one discussed her employment. I once, indeed, overheard part of a dialogue between Leah and one of the charwomen, of which Grace formed the subject. Leah had been saying something I had not caught, and the charwoman remarked:

"She gets good wages, I guess?"

"Yes," said Leah; "I wish I had as good. I should not wonder but Mrs. Poole has saved enough to keep her independent if she liked to leave; but I suppose she's got used to the place; and then she's not forty yet, and strong and able for anything."

"She is a good hand, I daresay," said the charwoman.

"Ah, she understands what she has to do—nobody better," rejoined Leah, "and it is not everyone could fill her shoes."

"That it is not!" was the reply. "I wonder whether master—"

The charwoman was going on, but here Leah turned and perceived me, and she gave her companion a nudge. "Doesn't she know?" I heard the woman whisper.

Leah shook her head, and the conversation was dropped. All I had gathered from it amounted to this—that there was a mystery at Thornfield, and that from participation in that mystery I was purposely excluded.

Thursday came. All work had been completed the previous evening: carpets were laid down, radiant white counterpanes spread, furniture rubbed; in the dining room, the sideboard flashed resplendent with plate; in the drawing room, vases of exotics bloomed on all sides. Afternoon arrived. Mrs. Fairfax assumed her best black satin gown, for it was her part to receive the company. Adèle, too, would be dressed. To please her, I allowed Sophie to apparel her in one of her short, full muslin frocks. For myself, I needed to make no change; I should not be called upon to quit my sanctum of the schoolroom.

It had been a mild, serene spring day; one of those days which, towards the end of March or the beginning of April, rise shining over the earth as heralds of summer. The evening was even warm, and I sat at work in the schoolroom with the window open.

"It gets late," said Mrs. Fairfax, entering in rustling state. "I am glad I ordered dinner an hour after the time Mr. Rochester mentioned, for it is past six now. I have sent John down to the gates to see if there is anything on the road from Millcote." She went to the window. "Here he is!" said she. "Well, John"—leaning out—"any news?"

"They're coming, ma'am," was the answer. "They'll be here in ten minutes."

Adèle flew to the window. I followed, standing on one side, so that, screened by the curtain, I could see without being seen. The ten minutes John had given seemed long, but at last wheels were heard; four equestrians galloped up the drive, and after them came two open carriages. Fluttering veils and waving plumes filled the vehicles; two of the cavaliers were young, dashing-looking gentlemen; the third was Mr. Rochester, on his black horse, Mesrour, Pilot bounding before him. At his side rode a lady, and he and she were the first of the party. Her purple riding habit almost swept the ground, her veil streamed on the breeze; mingling with its folds and gleaming through them shone rich raven ringlets.

"Miss Ingram!" exclaimed Mrs. Fairfax, and away she hurried to her post below.

The cavalcade turned the angle of the house, and I lost sight of it. Adèle now petitioned to go down; but I took her on my knee and gave her to understand that she must not on any account think of venturing in sight of the ladies, either now or at any other time, unless expressly sent for.

A joyous stir was now audible in the hall: gentlemen's deep tones and ladies' silvery accents blended together, and distinguishable above all was the sonorous voice of the master of Thornfield Hall. Then light steps ascended the stairs; and there was a tripping through the gallery, and soft cheerful laughs, and opening and closing doors, and, for a time, a hush.

As Adèle was hungry, I sought a back stairs which conducted directly to the kitchen. All in that region was fire and commotion; the cook hung over her crucibles in a frame of mind and body threatening spontaneous combustion. The new servants that had been hired from Millcote were bustling about everywhere. Threading the chaos, I at last reached the larder; there I took possession of a cold chicken, a roll of bread and some tarts, and with this booty I made a hasty retreat. I had regained the gallery when an accelerated hum warned me that the ladies were about to issue from their chambers. I could not proceed to the schoolroom without passing some of their doors, so I stood still at one end.

Presently the chambers gave up their fair tenants one after another; each came out gaily and airily, with dress that gleamed lustrous through the dusk. For a moment they stood grouped together, conversing; they then descended the staircase. A moment later I found Adèle peeping through the schoolroom door. "What beautiful ladies!" cried she. "Oh, I wish I might go to them! Do you think Mr. Rochester will send for us by and by, after dinner?"

"No, indeed, I don't; Mr. Rochester has something else to think about. Never mind the ladies tonight; perhaps you will see them tomorrow. Here is your dinner."

She was really hungry, so the chicken and tarts served to divert her for a time. I allowed her to sit up much later than usual, for she declared she could not possibly go to sleep while people bustled about below. I told her stories as long as she would listen to them, and then for a change I took her out into the gallery. It amused her to look over the balustrade and watch the servants passing backwards and forwards. When the evening was far advanced, a sound of music issued from the drawing room; Adèle and I sat down on the top step of the stairs to listen. Presently a lady's voice blended with the rich tones of the instrument; the solo over, a duet followed, and then a glee. A joyous conversational murmur filled up the intervals. I listened long, till the clock struck eleven. I looked at Adèle; her eyes were waxing heavy, so I carried her off to bed. It was near one before the gentlemen and ladies sought their chambers.

The next day was as fine as its predecessor; it was devoted by the party to an excursion to some site in the neighborhood. They set out early in the forenoon; Miss Ingram, as before, was the only lady equestrian. Mr. Rochester galloped at her side; the two rode a little apart from the rest. I pointed out this circumstance to Mrs. Fairfax, who was standing at the window with me.

"You said it was not likely they should think of being married," said I, "but you see Mr. Rochester evidently prefers her to any of the other ladies."

"Yes; I daresay. No doubt he admires her."

"And she him," I added. "Look how she leans towards him. I wish I could see her face; I have never had a glimpse of it yet."

"You will see her this evening," answered Mrs. Fairfax. "I happened to remark to Mr. Rochester how much Adèle wished to be introduced to the ladies, and he said: 'Oh, let her come into the drawing room after dinner, and request Miss Eyre to accompany her.'"

"Yes—he said that from mere politeness. I need not go, I am sure," I answered.

"Well—I observed to him that as you were unused to company, I did not think you would like appearing before so gay a party— all strangers; and he replied, in his quick way: 'Nonsense! If she objects, tell her it is my particular wish; and if she resists, say I shall come and fetch her.'"

"Well, I will not give him trouble. Will these people remain long, do you think?"

"Perhaps two or three weeks, not more."

It was with some trepidation that I perceived the hour approach when I was to repair with my charge to the drawing room. Adèle had been in ecstasy all day, after hearing she was to be presented to the ladies in the evening; and it was not till Sophie commenced the operation of dressing her that she sobered down. By the time she had her curls arranged in well-smoothed clusters, her pink satin frock put on and her long sash tied, she looked as grave as any judge. When she was dressed, she sat demurely down in her little chair, taking care not to crease the satin skirt, and she assured me she would not stir till I was ready. This I quickly was: my best dress (the silver-gray one, purchased for Miss Temple's wedding, and never worn since) was soon put on; my hair was soon smoothed; my sole ornament, the pearl brooch, soon assumed. We descended.

Fortunately there was another entrance to the drawing room than that through the saloon where they were all seated at dinner. We found the apartment vacant; a large fire burning silently on the marble hearth, and wax candles shining in bright solitude amidst the exquisite flowers on the tables. The crimson curtain hung before the arch; slight as was the separation this drapery formed from the party in the adjoining saloon, they spoke in so low a key that nothing of their conversation could be distinguished. Adèle, who appeared to be still under the influence of a most solemnizing impression, sat down, without a word, on the footstool I pointed out to her. I retired to a window seat.

A soft sound of rising now became audible; the curtain was swept back; a band of ladies stood in the arch; they entered, and the curtain fell behind them.

There were but eight; yet somehow, as they flocked in, they gave the impression of a much larger number. All had a sweeping amplitude of array that seemed to magnify their persons as a mist magnifies the moon. I rose and curtsied to them; one or two bent their heads in return; the others only stared at me.

They dispersed about the room, reminding me, by the buoyancy of their movements, of a flock of plumy birds. Some of them threw themselves in half-reclining positions on the sofas and ottomans; some bent over the tables and examined books; the rest gathered in a group round the fire. All talked in a low but clear tone which seemed habitual to them. I knew their names afterwards, and may as well mention them now.

First, there was Mrs. Eshton and her two daughters. She had evidently been a handsome woman, and was well preserved still. Both daughters were fair as lilies. The elder, Amy, was naïve and childlike in face and manner. The second, Louisa, was taller and more elegant.

Lady Lynn was a large and stout personage of about forty, very erect, very haughty-looking. Mrs. Colonel Dent was, I thought, more ladylike. She had a slight figure and a pale, gentle face.

But the three most distinguished were the Dowager Lady Ingram and her daughters, Blanche and Mary. They were all three of the loftiest stature. Most people would have termed the dowager a splendid woman of her age, and so she was, no doubt, physically speaking; but then there was an expression of almost insupportable haughtiness in her bearing and countenance. A crimson velvet robe invested her (I suppose she thought) with a truly imperial dignity.

Blanche and Mary were of equal stature—straight and tall— and both were attired in spotless white. Mary was too slim for her height, but Blanche was molded like a Diana. I regarded her, of course, with special interest. As far as person went, she answered point for point Mrs. Fairfax's description. The noble bust, the sloping shoulders, the graceful neck, the dark eyes— but her face? Her face was like her mother's: the same low brow, the same high features, the same pride. Mary had a milder and more open countenance than Blanche; but Mary's face lacked expression, her eye luster; she had nothing to say, and having once taken her seat, remained fixed like a statue in its niche.

And did I now think Miss Ingram such a choice as Mr. Rochester would be likely to make? I could not tell—but that he *did* admire her, I already seemed to have obtained proof; to remove the last shade of doubt, it remained but to see them together.

You are not to suppose, reader, that Adèle has all this time been sitting motionless on the stool at my feet: no; when the ladies entered, she rose, advanced to meet them, made a stately curtsy, and said, with gravity, "Bon jour, mesdames."

And Miss Ingram had looked down at her with a mocking air, and exclaimed, "Oh, what a little puppet!"

Lady Lynn had remarked, "It is Mr. Rochester's ward, I suppose—the little French girl he was speaking of."

Mrs. Dent had kindly taken her hand, and given her a kiss. Amy and Louisa Eshton had cried out simultaneously, "What a love of a child!"

And then they had called her to a sofa, where she now sat between them, chattering alternately in French and broken English; absorbing not only the young ladies' attention but that of Mrs. Eshton and Lady Lynn, and getting spoilt to her heart's content.

At last coffee is brought in, and the gentlemen are summoned. I sit in the shade—if shade there be in this brilliantly lit apartment; the window curtain half hides me. Again the arch yawns: they come. The collective appearance of the gentlemen, like that of the ladies, is very imposing: they are all costumed in black; most of them are tall, some young. Henry and Frederick Lynn are very dashing sparks, indeed, and Colonel Dent is a fine soldierly man. Mr. Eshton, the magistrate of the district, is gentlemanlike: his hair is quite white, his eyebrows and whiskers still dark. Lord Ingram, like his sisters, is handsome, but he shares Mary's apathetic and listless look.

And where is Mr. Rochester?

He comes in last: I am not looking at the arch, yet I see him enter. I try to concentrate my attention on the meshes of the purse I am forming—I wish to think only of the work I have in my hands, to see only the silver beads and silk threads that lie in my lap; whereas, I distinctly behold his figure, and I inevitably recall the moment when I last saw it: just after I had rendered him what he deemed an essential service—and he, holding my hand, and looking down on my face, surveyed me with eyes that revealed a heart full and eager to overflow, in whose emotions I had a part. How near had I approached him at that moment! Yet now, how distant, how far estranged we were! I did not wonder when, without looking at me, he took a seat at the other side of the room and began conversing with some of the ladies.

No sooner did I see that his attention was riveted on them, and that I might gaze without being observed, than my eyes were drawn involuntarily to his face. I looked, and had an acute pleasure in looking—a precious, yet poignant pleasure.

Most true it is that "beauty is in the eye of the gazer." My master's colorless, olive face, square, massive brow, deep eyes, strong features, firm, grim mouth, were not beautiful, according to rule; but they were more than beautiful to me—they took my feelings from my own power and fettered them in his. I had not intended to love him: the reader knows I had wrought hard to extirpate from my soul the germs of love there detected; and now, at the first renewed view of him, they spontaneously revived, green and strong! He made me love him without looking at me.

Coffee is handed. The ladies, since the gentlemen entered, have become lively as larks. Colonel Dent and Mr. Eshton argue on politics; their wives listen. The two proud dowagers, Lady Lynn and Lady Ingram, talk with Sir George, a very big and fresh-looking country gentleman. Mr. Frederick Lynn had taken a seat beside Mary Ingram, and is showing her the engravings of a splendid volume; the tall and phlegmatic Lord Ingram leans on the chairback of little Amy Eshton; Henry Lynn has taken possession of an ottoman at the feet of Louisa; Adèle shares it with him. With whom will Blanche Ingram pair? She is standing alone at the table, bending gracefully over an album. She seems waiting to be sought; but she will not wait too long. Mr. Rochester stands solitary on the hearth as she confronts him, taking her station on the opposite side of the mantelpiece.

"Mr. Rochester, I thought you were not fond of children?"

"Nor am I."

"Then, what induced you to take charge of such a little doll as that?" pointing to Adèle. "Where did you pick her up?"

"I did not pick her up, she was left on my hands."

"You should have sent her to school."

"I could not afford it: schools are so dear."

"Why, I suppose you have a governess for her; I saw a person with her just now—is she gone? Oh, no, there she is still behind the window curtain. You pay her, of course; I should think it quite as expensive—more so, for you have them both to keep in addition."

I feared—or should I say, hoped?—the allusion to me would

make Mr. Rochester glance my way, and I involuntarily shrank further into the shade, but he never turned his eyes.

"I have not considered the subject," said he indifferently, looking straight before him.

"No—you men never do consider economy and common sense. You should hear Mama on the chapter of governesses. Mary and I have had, I should think, a dozen at least in our day; half of them detestable and the rest ridiculous—were they not, Mama?"

"Did you speak, my own?"

The young lady reiterated her question with an explanation.

"My dearest, don't mention governesses; the word makes me nervous. I have suffered a martyrdom from their incompetency and caprice!"

"I suppose, now," said Miss Ingram sarcastically, "we shall have an abstract of the memoirs of all the governesses extant. In order to avert such a visitation, I move the introduction of a new topic. Mr. Rochester, do you second my motion?"

"Madam, I support you on this point as on every other."

"Then on me be the onus of bringing it forward. Signor Eduardo, are you in voice tonight?"

"Donna Bianca, if you command it, I will be."

"Then, signor, I lay on you my sovereign behest to furbish up your lungs and other vocal organs, as they will be wanted on my royal service."

Miss Ingram, who had now seated herself at the piano, spreading out her snowy robes in queenly amplitude, commenced a brilliant prelude. Now is my time to slip away, thought I; but Mr. Rochester began to sing, and the tones that then severed the air arrested me. Mrs. Fairfax had said Mr. Rochester possessed a fine voice; he did—a mellow, powerful bass, into which he threw his own feeling, his own force.

I waited till the last deep and full vibration had expired—till the tide of talk, checked an instant, had resumed its flow; I then quitted my sheltered corner and made my exit into the hall. My sandal was loose; I stopped to tie it, kneeling down at the foot of the staircase. I heard the dining-room door unclose; a gentleman came out; rising hastily, I stood face to face with Mr. Rochester.

"How do you do?" he asked.

"I am very well, sir."

"Why did you not come and speak to me in the room?"

"I did not wish to disturb you, as you seemed engaged, sir."

"You have been getting a good deal paler than you were—as I saw at first sight. What is the matter?"

"Nothing at all, sir."

"Did you take any cold that night you half drowned me?"

"Not the least."

"Return to the drawing room; you are deserting too early."

"I am tired, sir."

He looked at me for a minute.

"And a little depressed," he said. "What about? Tell me."

"Nothing—nothing, sir. I am not depressed."

"But I affirm that you are: so much depressed that a few more words would bring tears to your eyes—indeed, they are there now, shining and swimming. If I had time, and was not in mortal dread of some prating prig of a servant passing, I would know what all this means. Well, tonight I excuse you; but understand that so long as my visitors stay, I expect you to appear in the drawing room every evening. Now go, and send Sophie for Adèle. Good night, my—" He stopped, bit his lip, and abruptly left me.

MERRY DAYS WERE THOSE at Thornfield Hall, and busy days too; how different from the first three months of stillness, monotony and solitude I had passed beneath its roof! All sad feelings seemed now driven from the house, all gloomy associations forgotten; there was life everywhere, movement all day long. Even when rain set in for some days, no damp seemed cast over enjoyment: indoor amusements only became more lively and varied, in consequence of the stop put to outdoor gaiety.

And now I saw all Mr. Rochester's attentions appropriated by a great lady, who scorned to touch me with the hem of her robes as she passed; who, if ever her dark and imperious eye fell on me by chance, would withdraw it instantly as from an object too mean to merit observation. I felt sure he would soon marry Miss Ingram—because I read daily in her a proud security in his intentions respecting her—because I witnessed hourly in him a style of courtship which, if careless and choosing rather to be sought than to seek, was yet, in its very carelessness, captivating.

There was nothing to cool or banish my love for him in these circumstances, though much to create despair. Much too, you will think, reader, to engender jealousy. But I was not jealous: Miss Ingram was too inferior to excite that feeling. Pardon this seeming paradox; I mean what I say. She was very showy, but she was not genuine; she had a fine person, many brilliant attainments, but her mind was poor, her heart barren by nature. She did not know the sensations of sympathy and pity; tenderness and truth were not in her. Too often she betrayed this by the undue vent she gave to a spiteful antipathy she had conceived against little Adèle: sometimes ordering her from the room, and always treating her with coldness.

Other eyes besides mine watched these manifestations of character—watched them shrewdly. Yes, the future bridegroom, Mr. Rochester himself, exercised over his intended a ceaseless surveillance, and it was from this guardedness of his, this obvious absence of passion in his sentiments towards her, that my ever torturing pain arose.

I saw he was going to marry her, for family, perhaps political reasons; because her rank and connections suited him. I felt he had not given her his love, and that her qualifications were ill-adapted to win from him that treasure. This was the point—this was where the nerve was touched: *she could not charm him.*

I have not yet said anything condemnatory of Mr. Rochester's project of marrying for interest and connections. The longer I considered the position and education of the parties, the less I felt justified in blaming either him or Miss Ingram for acting in conformity to ideas instilled into them, doubtless, from their childhood. But in other points, as well as this, I was growing very lenient to my master: I was forgetting all his faults, for which

I had once kept a sharp lookout. The sarcasm that had repelled, the harshness that had startled me once, were only like keen condiments in a choice dish: their presence was pungent, but their absence would be felt as comparatively insipid.

Meantime, while I thought only of my master and his future bride, the rest of the party were occupied with their own separate interests and pleasures. Sometimes all, as with one consent, suspended their byplay to observe and listen to the principal actors, for, after all, Mr. Rochester and Miss Ingram were the life and soul of the party. If he were absent from the room an hour, a dullness seemed to steal over the spirits of his guests, and his re-entrance was sure to give a fresh impulse to the conversation.

The want of his animating influence appeared to be peculiarly felt one day that he had been summoned to Millcote on business and was not likely to return till late. The afternoon was wet; a walk the party had proposed to take to see a gypsy camp, lately pitched on a common beyond Hay, was consequently deferred.

It was verging on dusk, and the clock had already given warning of the hour to dress for dinner, when little Adèle, who knelt by me in the drawing-room window seat, exclaimed:

"Voilà Monsieur Rochester, qui revient!"

I turned, and Miss Ingram darted forward from her sofa; a crunching of wheels, and a splashing tramp of horse hoofs became audible on the wet gravel. A post chaise was approaching.

"What can possess him to come home in that style?" said Miss Ingram. "He rode Mesrour, did he not, when he went out? And Pilot was with him—what has he done with the animals?"

The post chaise stopped; the driver rang the doorbell, and a gentleman alighted, but it was not Mr. Rochester; it was a tall, fashionable-looking stranger. Some parleying was audible in the hall, and soon the newcomer entered. He bowed to Lady Ingram, as the eldest lady present.

"It appears I come at an inopportune time, madam," said he, "when my friend, Mr. Rochester, is from home; but I arrive from a long journey, and I think I may presume so far on old acquaintance to install myself here till he returns."

His manner was polite; his age might be about Mr. Rochester's; his complexion was sallow. Otherwise he was a fine-looking man, at first sight especially. On closer examination, you detected something in his face that failed to please. His eye was large and well cut, but the life looking out of it was a tame, vacant life.

The sound of the dressing bell dispersed the party. It was not till after dinner that I saw him again; he then seemed quite at his ease. As I sat in my usual nook, I was able to gather that he was called Mr. Mason; then I learned that he was but just arrived in England, and that he came from some hot country. Presently the words Jamaica, Kingston, Spanish Town, indicated the West Indies as his residence; and it was with no little surprise I gathered, ere long, that he had there first seen and become acquainted with Mr. Rochester. I knew Mr. Rochester had been a traveler, but I thought the continent of Europe had bounded his wanderings. Till now I had never heard a hint given of visits to more distant shores.

I was pondering these things, when an incident broke the thread of my musings. The footman, having brought in coal to put on the fire, in going out stopped near Mr. Eshton's chair, and said something to him in a low voice. I heard only the words, "old woman," "quite troublesome."

"Tell her she shall be put in the stocks if she does not take herself off," replied the magistrate.

"No—stop!" interrupted Colonel Dent. "Don't send her away, Eshton; we might turn the thing to account; better consult the ladies." And speaking louder, he continued, "Ladies, you talked of going to Hay Common to visit the gypsy camp; Sam, here, says that one of the old Mother Bunches is in the servants' hall at this moment, and insists upon being brought in before 'the quality,' to tell them their fortunes. Would you like to see her?"

"What is she like?" inquired the Misses Eshton in a breath.

"A shockingly ugly old creature, miss; almost as black as a crock."

"Why, she's a real sorceress!" cried Frederick Lynn. "Let us have her in, of course."

"I cannot possibly countenance any such inconsistent proceeding," chimed in the Dowager Ingram.

"Indeed, Mama, but you can—and will," pronounced the haughty voice of Blanche. "I have a curiosity to hear my fortune told; therefore, Sam, order the beldame forwards."

"Yes—yes—yes!" cried all the young people, both ladies and gentlemen. "Let her come—it will be excellent sport!"

The footman went. Excitement instantly seized the whole party: a running fire of raillery and jests was proceeding when Sam returned. "She won't come now," said he. "She says it's not her mission to appear before the 'vulgar herd' (them's her words). I must show her into a room by herself, and then those who wish to consult her must go to her one by one; and she says she will see only single ladies."

"You see now, my queenly Blanche," began Lady Ingram, "she encroaches. Be advised, my angel girl—and—"

"Show her into the library, of course," cut in the "angel girl." "It is not my mission to listen to her before the vulgar herd either. Is there a fire in the library?"

"Yes, ma'am—but she looks such a tinkler."

"Cease that chatter, blockhead, and do my bidding!"

Again Sam vanished; and mystery, animation, expectation rose to full flow once more.

"She's ready now," said the footman, as he reappeared. "She wishes to know who will be her first visitor."

Miss Ingram rose solemnly. "I go first," she said, in a tone which might have befitted the leader of a forlorn hope, mounting a breach in the van of his men.

"Oh, my dearest! Pause—reflect!" was her mama's cry; but she swept past her in stately silence, passed through the door which Colonel Dent held open, and we heard her enter the library.

A comparative silence ensued. Miss Mary declared she felt, for her part, she would never dare venture. Amy and Louisa Eshton tittered, and looked a little frightened. The minutes passed slowly: fifteen were counted before the library door again opened. Miss Ingram returned to us.

"Well, Blanche?" said Lord Ingram.

"What do you think? Is she a real fortune-teller?" demanded the Misses Eshton.

"Now, now, good people," returned Miss Ingram, "don't press upon me. You seem by the importance you all ascribe to this matter absolutely to believe we have a genuine witch in the house. I have seen a gypsy vagabond; she has practiced in hackneyed fashion the science of palmistry, and told me what such people usually tell."

Miss Ingram took a book, leaned back in her chair, and so declined further conversation. I watched her for nearly half an hour; during all that time she never turned a page, and her face grew momently darker, and more sourly expressive of disappointment. She had obviously not heard anything to her advantage; and it seemed to me that she herself, notwithstanding her professed indifference, attached undue importance to whatever revelations had been made her.

Meantime, Mary Ingram, Amy and Louisa Eshton declared they dared not go alone; a negotiation was opened through Sam; and after much pacing to and fro, permission was at last extorted from the sibyl for the three to wait upon her in a body. Their visit was not so still as Miss Ingram's had been: we heard giggling and little shrieks proceeding from the library; and at the end of about twenty minutes they burst the door open, and came running across the hall.

"I'm sure she is something not right!" they cried, one and all. "She knows all about us!" and they sank breathless into seats. In the midst of the tumult, I heard a "hem" close at my elbow. I turned, and saw Sam.

"If you please, miss, the gypsy declares that there is another young single lady in the room, and she swears she will not go till she has seen all. I thought it must be you; what shall I tell her?"

"Oh, I will go by all means," I answered; and I was glad of the unexpected opportunity to gratify my much excited curiosity. I slipped out of the room, unobserved by any eye, and closed the door quietly behind me.

THE LIBRARY LOOKED TRANQUIL enough as I entered it, and the sibyl was seated snugly enough in an easy chair at the chimney corner. She had on a red cloak and a broad-brimmed gypsy hat, tied down with a striped handkerchief under the chin. An extinguished candle stood on the table; she was bending over the fire, and seemed reading in a little black book by the light of the blaze.

I stood on the rug and warmed my hands, which were rather cold with sitting at a distance from the drawing-room fire. The gypsy shut her book and slowly looked up; her hat brim partially shaded her face, yet I could see, as she raised it, that it was a strange one. It looked all brown and black: elf-locks bristled out from beneath a white band which passed under her chin; her eye confronted me at once, with a bold and direct gaze.

"Well, and you want your fortune told?" she said in a voice as decided as her glance, as harsh as her features.

"I don't care about it, mother; you may please yourself, but I ought to warn you, I have no faith."

"It's like your impudence to say so; I expected it of you; I heard it in your step as you crossed the threshold."

"Did you? You've a quick ear."

"I have; and a quick eye, and a quick brain. I need them when I've customers like you to deal with. Why don't you tremble?"

"I'm not cold."

"Why don't you turn pale?"

"I am not sick."

"Why don't you consult my art?"

"I'm not silly."

The old crone "nichered" a laugh under her bonnet; she then drew out a short black pipe, and lighting it began to smoke. Having indulged a while in this sedative, she said very deliberately:

"You are cold; you are sick; and you are silly."

"Prove it," I rejoined.

"I will, in few words. You are cold, because you are alone; no contact strikes the fire from you that is in you. You are sick, because the best of feelings, the highest and the sweetest given to man, keeps far away from you. You are silly, because, suffer as you may, you will not beckon it to approach."

She again put her pipe to her lips, and smoked with vigor.

"You might say all that to almost anyone who, you knew, lived as a solitary dependent in a great house," I said.

"I might say it to almost anyone, but would it be true of almost anyone? If you knew it, you are peculiarly situated: very near happiness; yes, within reach of it. The materials are all prepared; let them be once approached and bliss results."

"I don't understand enigmas."

"If you wish me to speak more plainly, show me your palm."

"And I must cross it with silver, I suppose?"

"To be sure."

I gave her a shilling and she told me to hold out my hand. She approached her face to the palm, and pored over it.

"It is too fine," said she. "I can make nothing of such a hand as that; almost without lines; besides, what is in a palm? Destiny is not written there, but in the face. Kneel, and lift up your head."

"Ah, now you are coming to reality," I said as I obeyed her. "I shall begin to put some faith in you presently."

I knelt within half a yard of her. She stirred the fire, so that a ripple of light broke from the coal; the glare, however, only threw her face into deeper shadow. Mine, it illumined.

"I wonder with what feelings you came to me tonight," she said, when she had examined me awhile. "I wonder what thoughts are busy in your heart during all the hours you sit in yonder room with the fine people flitting before you like shapes in a magic lantern."

"I feel tired often, sleepy sometimes, but seldom sad."

"Then you have some secret hope to buoy you up and please you with whispers of the future?"

"Not I. The utmost I hope is, to save money enough out of my earnings to set up a school someday in a little house rented by myself."

"A mean nutriment for the spirit to exist on; and sitting in that window seat (you see I know your habits)—"

"You have learned them from the servants."

"Ah, you think yourself sharp! Well, perhaps I have. To speak truth, I am acquainted with one of them—Mrs. Poole."

I started to my feet when I heard the name.

"Don't be alarmed," continued the strange being; "she's a safe hand, is Mrs. Poole; anyone may repose confidence in her. But, as I was saying, sitting in that window seat, do you think of nothing but your future school? Is there not one face you study? One figure whose movements you follow?"

"I like to observe all the faces, and all the figures."

"But do you never single one from the rest—or maybe, two?"

"I do, frequently, when the gestures or looks of a pair seem telling a tale. It amuses me to watch them."

"What tale do you like best to hear?"

"Oh, I have not much choice! They generally run on the same

theme—courtship, and promise to end in the same catastrophe—marriage."

"And do you like that monotonous theme?"

"Positively, I don't care about it; it is nothing to me."

"Nothing to you? When a lady, young, charming, and endowed with the gifts of rank and fortune, sits and smiles in the eyes of a gentleman you—"

"I what?"

"You know—and, perhaps, think well of."

"I don't know the gentlemen here."

"You don't know the gentlemen here? Will you say that of the master of the house?"

"He is not at home."

"A most ingenious quibble! He went to Millcote this morning, and will be back here tonight, or tomorrow; does that circumstance exclude him from the list of your acquaintance?"

"No; but I can scarcely see what Mr. Rochester has to do with the theme you had introduced."

"I was talking of ladies smiling into the eyes of gentlemen; and of late so many smiles have been shed into Mr. Rochester's eyes that they overflow like two cups filled above the brim. You have seen love, have you not? And, looking forward, you have seen him married, and beheld his bride happy?"

"Humph! Not exactly. Your witch's skill is rather at fault sometimes."

"What the devil have you seen, then?"

"Never mind. I came here to inquire, not to confess. Is it known that Mr. Rochester is to be married?"

"Yes; and to the beautiful Miss Ingram. No doubt they will be a superlatively happy pair. He must love such a handsome, noble, accomplished lady; and probably she loves him. Or, if not his person, at least his purse."

"Mother, I did not come to hear Mr. Rochester's fortune; I came to hear my own, and you have told me nothing of it."

"Your fortune is yet doubtful: when I examined your face, one trait contradicted another. Chance has meted you a measure of happiness. She has laid it carefully on one side for you. It depends on yourself to stretch out your hand, and take it up; but whether you will do so, is the problem I study. Kneel again on the rug."

I knelt. She did not stoop toward me, but only gazed, leaning back in her chair. She began muttering:

"The flame flickers in the eye; the eye looks soft and full of feeling; it is susceptible; an unconscious lassitude weighs on the lid. That signifies melancholy resulting from loneliness. As to the mouth, it delights at times in laughter; it is disposed to impart all that the brain conceives; though I daresay it would be silent on much the heart experiences. I see no enemy to a fortunate issue but in the brow, and that brow professes to say, 'I can live alone, if self-respect and circumstances require me so to do. I need not sell my soul to buy bliss. I have an inward treasure, born with me, which can keep me alive if all extraneous delights should be withheld.' The forehead declares, 'Reason sits firm and holds the reins, and she will not let the feelings burst away and hurry her to wild chasms.'

"Well said, forehead; your declaration shall be respected. I have formed my plans—right plans I deem them—and in them I have attended to the claims of conscience, the counsels of reason. I know how soon youth would fade and bloom perish, if, in the cup of bliss offered, but one dreg of shame, or one flavor of remorse were detected. That will do. I think I rave in a kind of exquisite delirium. So far I have governed myself thoroughly; farther might try me beyond my strength. Rise, Miss Eyre. Leave me; 'the play is played out.'"

Where was I? Did I wake or sleep? Had I been dreaming? The old woman's voice had changed; her accent, her gesture, were familiar to me as my own face in a glass. I got up, but did not go. I looked; I stirred the fire, and I looked again, but she drew her bonnet closer about her face. The flame illuminated her hand stretched out; roused now, I at once noticed that hand. It was no more the withered limb of eld than my own; it was a rounded, supple member, symmetrically turned; a broad ring flashed on the little finger, and stooping forward, I saw a gem I had seen a hundred times before. Again I looked at the face, which was no longer turned from me—on the contrary, the bonnet was doffed, the head advanced.

"Well, Jane, do you know me?" asked the familiar voice.

"Only take off the red cloak, sir, and then—"

"But the string is in a knot—help me."

"Break it, sir."

"There, then— 'Off, ye lendings!'" And Mr. Rochester stepped out of his disguise.

"Now, sir, what a strange idea!"

"But well carried out, eh? Don't you think so?"

"With the ladies you must have managed well, but you did not act the character of a gypsy with me."

"What character did I act? My own?"

"No, some unaccountable one. In short, I believe you have been trying to draw me out—or in; you have been talking nonsense to make me talk nonsense. It is scarcely fair, sir."

"Do you forgive me, Jane?"

"I cannot tell till I have thought it all over. If, on reflection, I find I have fallen into no great absurdity, I shall try to forgive you; but it was not right."

"Oh, you have been very correct—very careful, very sensible."

I reflected, and thought, on the whole, I had. It was a comfort.

"Well," said he, "what are you musing about? What does that grave smile signify?"

"Wonder and self-congratulation, sir. I have your permission to retire now, I suppose?"

"No; stay a moment, and tell me what the people in the drawing room yonder are doing."

"Discussing the gypsy, I daresay. Oh! Are you aware, Mr. Rochester, that a stranger has arrived here since you left this morning?"

"A stranger—no. I expected no one; is he gone?"

"No; he said he had known you long, and that he could take the liberty of installing himself here till you returned."

"Did he give his name?"

"His name is Mason, sir; he comes from Jamaica, I think."

Mr. Rochester was standing near me; he had taken my hand, as if to lead me to a chair. As I spoke, he gave my wrist a convulsive grip; the smile on his lips froze.

"Mason!" he said, in the tone one might fancy a speaking automaton to enunciate a word. "Mason!" he reiterated; and he went over the syllables three times, growing whiter than ashes.

"Do you feel ill, sir?" I inquired.

"Jane, I've got a blow; I've got a blow!" He staggered.

"Oh, lean on me, sir!"

"Jane, you offered me your shoulder once before; let me have it now."

"Yes, sir, yes, and my arm."

He sat down, and made me sit beside him. Holding my hand in both his own, he chafed it; gazing on me, at the same time, with the most troubled and dreary look. "My little friend!" said he. "I wish I were in a quiet island with only you, and trouble, and danger and hideous recollections removed from me."

"Can I help you, sir? I'd give my life to serve you."

"Jane, if aid is wanted, I'll seek it at your hands; I promise you that."

"Thank you, sir; tell me what to do. I'll try, at least, to do it."

"Fetch me now, Jane, a glass of wine from the dining room; and tell me what Mason is doing."

I went. I found all the party in the dining room. Supper was on the sideboard; each had taken what he chose, and they stood about in groups, their plates in their hands. Laughter and conversation were animated. Mr. Mason stood near the fire, talking to Colonel and Mrs. Dent, and appeared as merry as any of them. I filled a wineglass and returned to the library.

Mr. Rochester's extreme pallor had disappeared, and he looked once more firm and stern. He took the glass from my hand. "Here is to your health, ministrant spirit!" he said, swallowing the contents. "What are they doing, Jane?"

"Laughing and talking, sir."

"They don't look grave and mysterious, as if they had heard something strange?"

"Not at all."

"If all these people came in a body and spat at me, what would you do, Jane?"

"Turn them out of the room, sir, if I could."

He half smiled. "But if I were to go to them, and they only looked at me coldly, and then dropped off and left me one by one, what then? Would you go with them?"

"I rather think not, sir. I should have more pleasure in staying with you."

"To comfort me?"

"Yes, sir, to comfort you as well as I could."

"Go back now into the room; step quietly up to Mason, and whisper in his ear that Mr. Rochester is come and wishes to see him; show him in here and then leave me."

"Yes, sir."

I did his behest. The company all stared at me as I passed straight among them. I delivered the message to Mr. Mason, ushered him into the library, and then I went upstairs.

At a late hour, I heard the visitors repair to their chambers. I distinguished Mr. Rochester's voice, and heard him say, "This way, Mason; this is your room."

He spoke cheerfully; the gay tones set my heart at ease. I was soon asleep.

CHAPTER VIII

I HAD FORGOTTEN TO DRAW my curtain, which I usually did; the consequence was, that when the moon, which was full and bright, came opposite my casement and looked in at me, her gaze roused me. I half rose, and stretched my arm to draw the curtain.

Good God! What a cry!

The night—its silence—its rest, was rent in twain by a savage, a sharp, a shrilly sound that ran from end to end of Thornfield Hall. My pulse stopped, my heart stood still. The cry died, and was not renewed.

It came out of the third story, for it passed overhead. And overhead—yes, in the room just above mine—I now heard a struggle; a deadly one it seemed; and a half-smothered voice shouted:

"Help! Help! Help!" three times rapidly.

"Will no one come?" it cried; and then, while the staggering and stamping went on wildly, I distinguished through plank and plaster:

"Rochester! Rochester! For God's sake, come!"

A chamber door opened; someone rushed along the gallery. Another step stamped on the flooring above and something fell; and there was silence.

I put on some clothes, though horror shook all my limbs; I issued from my apartment. The sleepers were all aroused: ejaculations, terrified murmurs sounded in every room; one looked out and another looked out. Gentlemen and ladies alike had quitted their beds, and "Oh! what is it?" "Who is hurt?" "Are there robbers?" was demanded confusedly on all hands. But for the moonlight they would have been in complete darkness. They ran to and fro; the confusion was inextricable.

"Where the devil is Rochester?" cried Colonel Dent. "I cannot find him in his bed."

"Here! Here!" was shouted in return. "Be composed, all of you; I'm coming."

And the door at the end of the gallery opened, and Mr. Rochester advanced with a candle. One of the ladies ran to him directly; it was Miss Ingram. "What awful event has taken place?" said she. "Speak! Let us know the worst at once!"

Mr. Rochester's black eyes darted sparks. Calming himself by an effort, he said, "A servant has had a nightmare, that is all. She's an excitable, nervous person, and has taken a fit with fright. Now then, I must see you all back into your rooms, for, till the house is settled, she cannot be looked after. Gentlemen, have the goodness to set the ladies the example."

And so, by dint of coaxing and commanding, he contrived to get them all once more enclosed in their separate dormitories. I did not wait to be ordered back to mine, but retreated unnoticed.

Not, however, to go to bed; on the contrary, I dressed myself. The sounds I had heard after the scream had probably been heard only in my room; but they assured me that it was not a servant's dream which had thus struck horror through the house. I dressed, then, to be ready for emergencies, and sat by the window, looking out over the silent grounds and silvered fields.

Stillness returned: each murmur and movement ceased gradually, and in about an hour Thornfield Hall was again as hushed as a desert. Meantime the moon declined; she was about to set when a cautious hand tapped low at my door.

"Am I wanted?" I asked.

"Are you up?" asked my master.

"Yes, sir."

"Come out, then, quietly."

I obeyed. Mr. Rochester stood in the gallery, holding a light. "I want you," he said. "Come this way, and make no noise."

My slippers were thin; I could walk the matted floor as softly as a cat. He glided up the gallery and up the stairs, and stopped in the dark, low corridor of the fateful third story.

"Have you a sponge and any volatile salts in your room?" he asked in a whisper.

"Yes, sir."

"Go back and fetch both."

I fetched them and retraced my steps. He still waited; approaching one of the small, black doors, he put a key in the lock; he paused and addressed me again.

"You don't turn sick at the sight of blood?"

"I think I shall not. I have never been tried yet."

"Just give me your hand," he said; "it will not do to risk a fainting fit." I put my fingers into his. "Warm and steady," was his remark. He turned the key and opened the door.

I saw a room I remembered to have seen the day Mrs. Fairfax showed me over the house: it was hung with tapestry, but the tapestry was now looped up on one part, and there was a door apparent, which had then been concealed. This door was open; I heard thence a snarling, snatching sound, almost like a dog quarreling. Mr. Rochester, putting down his candle, said to me, "Wait a minute," and he went forward to the inner apartment. A shout of laughter greeted his entrance; noisy at first, and terminating in Grace Poole's own goblin ha! ha! *She* then was there. He made some sort of arrangement, without speaking, though I heard a low voice address him; he came out and closed the door behind him.

"Here, Jane!" he said; and I walked round to the other side of a large bed, which with its drawn curtains concealed a considerable portion of the chamber. An easy chair was near the bed-head; a man sat in it, dressed with the exception of his coat; his head leaned back; his eyes were closed. Mr. Rochester held the candle over him; I recognized in his pale and seemingly lifeless face—the stranger, Mason; I saw too that his linen on one side, and one arm, was almost soaked in blood.

"Hold the candle," said Mr. Rochester, and I took it; he fetched a basin of water from the washstand. "Hold that," said he. I obeyed. He took the sponge and moistened the corpselike face; he applied my smelling bottle to the nostrils. Mr. Mason shortly unclosed his eyes; he groaned. Mr. Rochester opened the shirt of the wounded man, whose arm and shoulder were bandaged, and sponged away blood, trickling down.

"Is there immediate danger?" murmured Mr. Mason.

"Pooh! No—a mere scratch. I'll fetch a surgeon for you now; you'll be able to be removed by morning. Jane," he continued.

"Sir?"

"I shall have to leave you in this room with this gentleman, for perhaps two hours; you will sponge the blood when it returns; if he feels faint, you will put the glass of water to his lips, and your salts to his nose. You will not speak to him on any pretext—and, Richard, it will be at the peril of your life if you speak to her: agitate yourself and I'll not answer for the consequences."

Again the poor man groaned; he looked as if he dared not move; fear, either of death or of something else, appeared almost to paralyze him. Mr. Rochester put the now bloody sponge into my hand, and watched me use it a second; then saying, "Remember!

No conversation," he left the room. I experienced a strange feeling as the key grated in the lock, and the sound of his retreating step ceased to be heard.

Here then I was in the third story, fastened into one of its mystic cells; a bloody spectacle under my eyes and hands; a murderess hardly separated from me by a single door. I shuddered at the thought of Grace Poole bursting out upon me. And this quiet stranger I bent over—how had he become involved in the web of horror? What made him seek this quarter of the house when he should have been asleep in bed? And why did he so quietly submit to the concealment Mr. Rochester enforced? I saw that Mr. Mason was submissive to Mr. Rochester; whence then had arisen Mr. Rochester's dismay when he heard of Mr. Mason's arrival?

"When will he come? When will he come?" I cried inwardly, as the night lingered and lingered—as my bleeding patient drooped, moaned, sickened, and neither day nor aid arrived. The candle, wasted at last, went out; as it expired, I perceived streaks of gray light edging the window curtains.

Presently I heard Pilot bark far below; hope revived. In five minutes more the grating key warned me my watch was relieved. It could not have lasted more than two hours; many a week has seemed shorter.

Mr. Rochester entered, and with him the surgeon he had fetched. "Now, Carter, be on the alert," he said to this last. "I give you but half an hour for dressing the wound, getting the patient downstairs and all."

Mr. Rochester drew back the curtain to let in the daylight; and I was surprised and cheered to see how far dawn was advanced. Then he approached Mason, whom the surgeon was already handling. "Now, my good fellow, how are you?" he asked.

"She's done for me, I fear," was the faint reply.

"Not a whit! Courage! You've lost a little blood, that's all. Carter, assure him there's no danger."

"I can do that conscientiously," said Carter, who had now undone the bandages; "but how is this? The flesh on the shoulder is torn as well as cut. There have been teeth here!"

"She bit me," he murmured. "She worried me like a tigress, when Rochester got the knife from her."

"You should have grappled with her at once," said Mr. Rochester. "I warned you: I said—be on your guard when you go near her."

"I thought I could have done some good."

"You thought! You thought! Yes; it makes me impatient to hear you; but, however, you are likely to suffer enough for not taking my advice, so I'll say no more. Carter—hurry! The sun will soon rise, and I must have him off."

"Directly, sir; the shoulder is just bandaged. I must look to this other wound in the arm; she has had her teeth here too, I think."

"She sucked the blood; she said she'd drain my heart," said Mason.

I saw Mr. Rochester shudder; a marked expression of horror warped his countenance; but he only said, "Come, be silent, Richard, and never mind her gibberish. You will forget it; when you get back to Spanish Town, you may think of her as dead and buried—or rather, you need not think of her at all."

"Impossible to forget this night!"

"It is not impossible: have some energy, man. There! Carter has done with you; I'll make you decent in a trice. Jane—" he turned to me for the first time since his re-entrance; "go down into my dressing room; open the top drawer of the wardrobe and take out a clean shirt and neck handkerchief; bring them here and be nimble."

I went, found the articles named, and returned with them.

"Was anybody stirring below when you went down, Jane?" inquired Mr. Rochester.

"No, sir; all was very still."

"We shall get you off cannily, Dick. I have striven long to avoid exposure, and I should not like it to come at last. Here, Carter, help him on with his waistcoat. Where did you leave your furred cloak? You can't travel a mile without that, I know, in this damned cold climate. In your room? Jane, run down to Mr.

Mason's room—the one next mine—and fetch a cloak you will see there."

Again I ran, and again returned, bearing an immense mantle lined and edged with fur. Dressed now, Mr. Mason still looked pale, but he was no longer gory and sullied. Mr. Rochester took his arm.

"Now I am sure you can get on your feet," he said. "Try."

The patient rose.

"Carter, take him under the other shoulder. Be of good cheer, Richard; step out—that's it!"

"I do feel better," remarked Mr. Mason.

"I am sure you do. Now, Jane, trip on before us to the back stairs, unbolt the side-passage door, and tell the driver of the post chaise you will see outside to be ready; and, Jane, if anyone is about, come to the foot of the stairs and hem."

It was by this time half past five, and the sun was on the point of rising; but I found the kitchen still dark and silent. The side-passage door was fastened, but the gates stood wide open, and there was a post chaise stationed outside. I approached the driver, and said the gentlemen were coming. The stillness of early morning slumbered everywhere; the curtains were yet drawn over the servants' chamber windows; little birds were just twittering in the blossom-blanched orchard trees.

The gentlemen now appeared. Mason, supported by Mr. Rochester and the surgeon, seemed to walk with tolerable ease. They assisted him into the chaise; Carter followed.

"Take care of him," said Mr. Rochester to the latter, "and keep him at your house till he is quite well; I shall ride over in a day or two to see how he gets on. Richard, how is it with you?"

"The fresh air revives me, Fairfax."

"Good-by, then, Dick."

"Fairfax—let her be taken care of; let her be treated as tenderly as may be; let her—" He stopped and burst into tears.

"I do my best; and have done it, and will do it," was the answer; he shut up the chaise door, and the vehicle drove away.

"Yet would to God there was an end of all this!" added Mr.

Rochester, as he moved with abstracted air towards a door in the wall bordering the orchard. I prepared to return to the house; again, however, I heard him call "Jane!"

"Come where there is some freshness, for a few moments," he said; "that house is a dungeon. Don't you feel it so?"

"It seems to me a splendid mansion, sir."

"The glamour of inexperience is over your eyes," he answered; "you cannot discern that the gilding is slime and the silk draperies cobwebs. Now *here*"—he pointed to the leafy enclosure we had entered—"all is real, sweet and pure."

He strayed down a walk edged with box; with apple trees, pear trees and cherry trees on one side, and a border on the other, full of old-fashioned flowers, stocks, sweet Williams, primroses, pansies and various fragrant herbs. They were fresh now as a succession of April showers and gleams, followed by a lovely spring morning, could make them.

"Jane, will you have a flower?"

He gathered a half-blown rose and offered it to me.

"Thank you, sir."

"You have passed a strange night, Jane, and it has made you look pale. Were you afraid when I left you alone with Mason?"

"I was afraid of someone coming out of the inner room."

"But I had fastened the door. I should have been a careless shepherd if I had left a lamb—my pet lamb—so near a wolf's den, unguarded: you were safe."

"Will Grace Poole live here still, sir?"

"Oh, yes! Don't trouble your head about her."

"Is the danger you apprehended last night gone by now, sir?"

"I cannot vouch for that till Mason is out of England, nor even then. To live, for me, Jane, is to stand on a crater crust which may crack and spew fire any day."

"But Mr. Mason seems a man easily led. Your influence, sir, is evidently potent with him: he will never willfully injure you."

"Oh, no! Mason will not knowingly hurt me—but unintentionally he might, by one careless word, deprive me, if not of life, yet forever of happiness."

"Tell him to be cautious, sir; let him know what you fear, and show him how to avert the danger."

He laughed sardonically, hastily took my hand, and as hastily threw it from him.

"If I could do that, simpleton, where would the danger be? But I cannot give Mason orders in this case; for it is imperative that I should keep him ignorant that harm to me is possible. Now you look puzzled; and I will puzzle you farther. You are my little friend, are you not?"

"I like to serve you, sir, and to obey you in all that is right."

"Precisely: I see you do. I see genuine contentment in your eye and face when you are helping me and pleasing me—working for me, and with me, in, as you characteristically say, '*all that is right*': for if I bid you do what you thought was wrong, there would be no light-footed running, no neat-handed alacrity, no lively glance and animated complexion. My friend would then turn to me, quiet and pale, and would say, 'No, sir, I cannot do it, because it is wrong.' Well, you too have power over me, and may injure me; yet I dare not show you where I am vulnerable, lest, faithful and friendly as you are, you should transfix me at once."

"If you have no more to fear from Mr. Mason than you have from me, sir, you are very safe."

"God grant it may be so! Here, Jane, is an arbor; sit down."

The arbor was an arch in the wall, lined with ivy; it contained a rustic seat. Mr. Rochester took it, leaving room for me; but I stood before him. "Sit," he said; "the bench is long enough for two. You don't hesitate to take a place at my side, do you?"

I answered him by assuming it.

"Now, my little friend, while the sun drinks the dew—while all the flowers in this old garden awake, and the birds fetch their young ones' breakfast, I'll put a case to you, which you must endeavor to suppose your own. But first, look at me, and tell me you are at ease."

"I am content."

"Well, then, Jane, call to aid your fancy. Suppose you were no longer a girl well reared and disciplined, but a wild boy indulged from childhood upwards; imagine yourself in a remote foreign land; conceive that you there commit a capital error, one whose consequences must follow you through life. The results of what you have done become in time to you utterly insupportable; you take measures to obtain relief—unusual measures, but neither unlawful nor culpable. Still you are miserable; you wander here and there, seeking rest in exile, happiness in heartless, sensual pleasure—such as dulls intellect and blights feeling.

"Heart-weary and soul-withered, you come home after years of voluntary banishment; you make a new acquaintance; you find in this stranger much of the good and bright qualities which you have sought for twenty years, and never before encountered. Such society regenerates. You feel better days come back—higher wishes, purer feelings; you desire to spend what remains to you of life in a way more worthy of an immortal being. To attain this end, are you justified in overleaping an obstacle of custom—a conventional impediment, which neither your conscience sanctifies nor your judgment approves?"

He paused for an answer: and what was I to say? Oh, for some good spirit to suggest a judicious response! The west wind whispered in the ivy round me; the birds sang in the treetops; but their song, however sweet, was inarticulate.

Again Mr. Rochester propounded his query: "Is the sinful but now repentant man justified in daring the world's opinion, in order to attach to him forever this gentle, gracious stranger?"

"Sir," I answered, "a sinner's reformation should never depend on a fellow creature. If anyone you know has suffered and erred, let him look higher than his equals for strength and solace."

"But the instrument—the instrument! God, who does the work, ordains the instrument. I have myself been a worldly, dissipated man, and I believe I have found the instrument for my cure, in—"

He paused; the birds went on caroling, the leaves lightly rustling. I almost wondered they did not check their songs and whispers to catch the suspended revelation, but they would have had to wait many minutes—so long was the silence protracted. At last I looked up at the tardy speaker; he was looking eagerly at me.

"Little friend," said he, in quite a changed tone—while his face changed too; losing all its softness and gravity, and becoming harsh and sarcastic—"you have noticed my tender penchant for Miss Ingram: don't you think if I married her she would regenerate me with a vengeance?"

He got up instantly, went quite to the other end of the walk, and when he came back he was humming a tune.

"Jane, Jane," said he, stopping before me, "you are quite pale with your vigils; don't you curse me for disturbing your rest?"

"Curse you? No, sir."

"Shake hands in confirmation of the word. What cold fingers! They were warmer last night when I touched them at the door of the mysterious chamber. Jane, when will you watch with me again?"

"Whenever I can be useful, sir."

"For instance, the night before I am married! I am sure I shall not be able to sleep. Will you promise to sit up with me to bear me company? To you I can talk of my lovely one, for now you have seen her and know her."

"Yes, sir."

"She's a rare one, is she not, Jane?"

"Yes, sir."

"A strapper—a real strapper, Jane: big, brown and buxom. Bless me! There's Dent and Lynn in the stables! Go in by the shrubbery, through that wicket."

As I went one way, he went another, and I heard him in the yard, saying cheeringly, "Mason got the start of you all this morning; he was gone before sunrise. I rose at four to see him off."

CHAPTER IX

THAT AFTERNOON I WAS SUMMONED downstairs by a message that someone wanted me in Mrs. Fairfax's room. On repairing thither I found a servant waiting for me. He was dressed in deep mourning, and the hat in his hand bore a crape band.

"I daresay you hardly remember me, Miss," he said, "but my name is Leaven. I was coachman with Mrs. Reed when you were at Gateshead, and I work there still."

"Oh, Robert! How do you do? I remember you very well. And how is Bessie? You are married to Bessie?"

"Yes, Miss. My wife is very hearty, thank you; she brought me another little one two months since."

"And are the family well at the house, Robert?"

"I am sorry I can't give you better news of them, Miss: they are in great trouble at present."

"I hope no one is dead," I said, glancing at his black dress.

He looked down and replied, "Mr. John died yesterday was a week, at his chambers in London."

"Mr. John? And how does his mother bear it?"

"Why, you see, Miss Eyre, it is not a common mishap. His life has been very wild; his death was shocking."

"I heard from Bessie he was not doing well."

"Doing well! He ruined his health and his estate amongst the worst men and women. He got into debt and into jail; his mother helped him out twice, but as soon as he was free he returned to his old habits. He came down to Gateshead three weeks ago and wanted Missis to give up all to him. Missis refused, so he went back, and the next news was that he was dead. They say he killed himself."

I was silent: the tidings were frightful. Robert Leaven resumed:

"Missis had been out of health herself for some time; she had got very stout, and the information about Mr. John's death brought on a stroke. She was three days without speaking, but last Tuesday she seemed better; she appeared as if she wanted to say something. It was only yesterday morning, however, that Bessie understood she was pronouncing your name; and at last she made out the words, 'Fetch Jane Eyre: I want to speak to her.' Bessie told Miss Reed and Miss Georgiana, and advised them to send for you, and at last they consented. If you can get ready, Miss, I should like to take you back with me early tomorrow morning."

"Yes, Robert, I shall be ready: it seems to me I ought to go."

"I suppose you will have to ask leave, Miss?"

"Yes; and I will do it now;" and having directed Robert to the servants' hall, I went in search of Mr. Rochester.

I asked Mrs. Fairfax if she had seen him; yes, she believed he was playing billiards with Miss Ingram. To the billiard room I hastened. Mr. Rochester, Miss Ingram, the two Misses Eshton and their admirers, were all busied in the game, and I approached the master where he stood at Miss Ingram's side. She turned as I drew near, and looked at me haughtily; her eyes seemed to demand, "What can the creeping creature want now?" and she made a movement as if tempted to order me away.

"Does that person want you?" she inquired of Mr. Rochester; and Mr. Rochester turned to see who the "person" was. He made a curious grimace, threw down his cue and followed me from the room.

"Well, Jane?" he said.

"If you please, sir, I want leave of absence for a week or two, to see a sick lady who has sent for me."

"What sick lady? Where does she live?"

"At Gateshead, in ——shire."

"——shire? That is a hundred miles off! Who may she be that sends for people to see her that distance?"

"Her name is Reed, sir, Mrs. Reed."

"Reed? There was a Reed of Gateshead, a magistrate."

"It is his widow, sir."

"And what have you to do with her?"

"Mr. Reed was my uncle, my mother's brother."

"The deuce he was! You never told me that before; you always said you had no relations."

"None that would own me, sir. Mr. Reed is dead, and his wife cast me off."

"But Reed left children? Sir George Lynn was talking of a Reed of Gateshead, yesterday—who, he said, was a rascal."

"John Reed is dead, sir: he is supposed to have committed suicide. The news so shocked his mother that it brought on an apoplectic attack."

"And what good can you do her? Nonsense, Jane! I would never run a hundred miles to see an old lady who will, perhaps, be dead before you reach her. Besides, you say she cast you off."

"Yes, sir, but that is long ago; I could not be easy to neglect her wishes now."

"How long will you stay?"

"As short a time as possible, sir."

"Promise me only to stay a week—"

"I had better not pass my word. I might be obliged to break it."

"At all events you *will* come back: you will not be induced under any pretext to take up a permanent residence with her?"

"Oh no! I shall certainly return if all be well."

Mr. Rochester meditated. "When do you wish to go?"

"Early tomorrow morning, sir."

"Well, you must have some money; you can't travel without it, and I daresay you have not much: I have given you no salary yet. How much have you in the world, Jane?" he asked, smiling.

I drew out my purse; a meager thing it was. "Five shillings, sir." He took the purse, poured the hoard into his palm and chuckled over it as if its scantiness pleased him. Soon he produced his pocketbook. "Here," said he, offering me a note; it was fifty pounds, and he owed me but fifteen. I told him I had no change.

"I don't want change; take your wages."

I declined accepting more than was my due. He scowled at first; then, as if recollecting something, he said:

"Right, right! Better not give you all now; you would, perhaps, stay away three months if you had fifty pounds. There are ten; is it not plenty?"

"Yes, sir, but now you owe five."

"Come back for it then."

"Mr. Rochester, I may as well mention another matter of business to you while I have the opportunity. You have as good as informed me, sir, that you are going shortly to be married?"

"Yes. What then?"

"In that case, sir, Adèle ought to go to school."

"To get her out of my bride's way, who might otherwise walk

over her. There's sense in the suggestion. And you, of course, must march straight to—the devil?"

"I hope not, sir; but I must seek another situation somewhere."

"Jane!"

"Sir?"

"Promise me one thing: to trust this quest of a situation to me. I'll find you one in time."

"I shall be glad so to do, sir, if you, in your turn, will promise that Adèle and I shall be both safe out of the house before your bride enters it."

"Very well! I'll pledge my word on it. You go tomorrow, then, and you and I must bid good-by for a little while?"

"I suppose so, sir."

"And how do people perform that ceremony of parting, Jane? Teach me; I'm not quite up to it."

"They say farewell, or any other form they prefer."

"Then say it."

"Farewell, Mr. Rochester, for the present."

"Farewell, Miss Eyre, for the present. Is that all?"

"Yes."

"It seems dry, and unfriendly, to my notions. I should like something else—if one shook hands, for instance. But no, that would not content me either. So you'll do no more than say farewell, Jane?"

"It is enough, sir; as much goodwill may be conveyed in one word as in many."

The dinner bell rang then, and suddenly away he bolted, without another syllable. I saw him no more during the day, and was off before he had risen in the morning.

I reached the lodge at Gateshead about five o'clock in the afternoon of the first of May; I stepped in there before going up to the hall. Bessie sat on the hearth, nursing her last-born, and her son Bobby and his sister played quietly in a corner.

"Bless you! I knew you would come!" exclaimed Mrs. Leaven.

"Yes, Bessie," said I, after I had kissed her; "and I trust I am not too late. How is Mrs. Reed?"

"More sensible and collected than she was. The doctor says she may linger a week yet; but he hardly thinks she will recover."

"Has she mentioned me lately?"

"She was talking of you only this morning, but she is sleeping now. She generally lies in a kind of lethargy all afternoon, and wakes up about six or seven. Will you rest yourself here an hour, Miss, and then I will go up with you?"

Robert here entered, and Bessie laid her child in the cradle and went to welcome him; afterwards she insisted on my having some tea, for she said I looked pale and tired.

Old times crowded fast back on me as I watched Bessie bustling about—setting out the tea tray with her best china, cutting bread and butter, toasting a tea cake, and, betweenwhiles, giving little Robert or Jane an occasional tap or push, just as she used to give me in former days. Tea ready, I was going to approach the table; but she desired me to sit still, quite in her old, peremptory tones. I must be served at the fireside, she said; and she placed before me a little round stand with my cup and a plate of toast, absolutely as she used to accommodate me with some privately purloined dainty on a nursery chair, and I smiled and obeyed her as in by-gone days.

An hour was soon gone. Bessie restored to me my bonnet, etc., and, accompanied by her, I quitted the lodge to walk to the hall. On a dark, misty, raw morning in January, almost nine years before, I had left that hostile roof with a desperate and embittered heart. The same hostile roof now again rose before me; I had yet an aching heart, and I still felt as a wanderer on the face of the earth; but I experienced firmer trust in my own powers, and the gaping wound of my wrongs was now quite healed.

"You shall go into the breakfast room first," said Bessie, as she preceded me through the hall; "the young ladies will be there."

In another moment I was within that apartment. There was every article of furniture looking just as it did on the morning I was first introduced to Mr. Brocklehurst: the very rug he had stood upon still covered the hearth. The inanimate objects were not changed, but the living things had altered past recognition.

Two young ladies appeared before me, one very tall and thin, with a sallow face and severe mien. This I felt sure was Eliza, though I could trace little resemblance to her former self in that colorless visage. The other was as certainly Georgiana, but not the Georgiana I remembered—the slim and fairylike girl of eleven. This was a full-blown, very plump damsel, fair as waxwork, with handsome features, languishing blue eyes, and ringleted yellow hair.

Both ladies rose to welcome me, and both addressed me as "Miss Eyre." Eliza's greeting was delivered in a short, abrupt voice, without a smile; and then she sat down again and seemed to forget me. Georgiana added to her "How d'ye do" several commonplaces about my journey, the weather and so on, uttered in rather a drawling tone, and accompanied by sundry side glances that measured me from head to foot. A sneer, however, had now no longer that power over me it once possessed: as I sat between my cousins, I was surprised to find how easy I felt under the total neglect of the one and the semisarcastic attentions of the other.

"How is Mrs. Reed?" I asked soon, looking at Georgiana.

"Mrs. Reed? Ah! Mama you mean; she is extremely poorly; I doubt if you can see her tonight."

"If," said I, "you would just step upstairs and tell her I am come, I should be much obliged to you."

Georgiana almost started. "I know she had a particular wish to see me," I added, "and I should not defer attending to her desire longer than is absolutely necessary."

"Mama dislikes being disturbed in an evening," remarked Eliza.

I soon rose, and said I would just step out to Bessie, and ask her to ascertain whether Mrs. Reed was disposed to receive me tonight. I had taken a journey of a hundred miles to see my aunt, and I must stay with her till she was better—or dead; as to her daughters' pride and folly, I must put it on one side. So I addressed the housekeeper, told her I should probably be a visitor for a week or two, and had my trunk conveyed to my chamber; then I met Bessie on the landing.

"Missis is awake," said she; "come and let us see if she will know you."

I did not need to be guided to the room. I hastened before Bessie, I softly opened the door. There was the great four-post bed with amber hangings as of old; there the footstool at which I had a hundred times been sentenced to kneel, to ask pardon for offenses. I approached the bed and leaned over the high-piled pillows.

Well did I remember Mrs. Reed's face, and I eagerly sought the familiar image. I had left this woman in bitterness and hate, and I came back to her now with no other emotion than a sort of ruth for her great sufferings, and a strong yearning to forget and forgive all injuries—to clasp hands in amity.

The well-known face was there: stern, relentless as ever—there was that peculiar eye which nothing could melt; how often had it lowered on me in menace and hate! And yet I stooped down and kissed her: she looked at me. "Is this Jane Eyre?" she said.

"Yes, Aunt Reed. How are you, dear Aunt?"

I had once vowed that I would never call her aunt again; I thought it no sin to break that vow now. My fingers had fastened on her hand which lay outside the sheet; had she pressed mine kindly, I should at that moment have experienced true pleasure.

But unimpressionable natures are not so soon softened: Mrs. Reed took her hand away, and regarded me icily. I felt pain, and then I felt ire; and then I felt a determination to subdue her. My tears had risen, just as in childhood; I ordered them back to their source, I brought a chair to the bedhead and sat down.

"You sent for me," I said, "and I am here; and it is my intention to stay till I see how you get on."

"You may tell my daughters I wish you to stay till I can talk some things over with you I have on my mind. Tonight it is too late, and I have difficulty in recalling them. But there was something I wished to say—let me see—"

The wandering look and changed utterance told what wreck had taken place in her once-vigorous frame. Turning restlessly, she drew the bedclothes round her; my elbow, resting on a corner of the quilt, fixed it down; she was at once irritated.

"Sit up!" said she. "Don't annoy me with holding the clothes fast—are you Jane Eyre?"

"I am Jane Eyre."

"I have had more trouble with that child than anyone would believe. So much annoyance as she caused me! What did they do with her at Lowood? The fever broke out there, and many died. She, however, did not die, but I said she did—I wish she had!"

"A strange wish, Mrs. Reed; why do you hate her so?"

"I had a dislike to her mother always; for she was my husband's only sister, and a great favorite with him: when news came of her death, he wept like a simpleton. He would send for the baby; and I hated it the first time I set my eyes on it—a sickly, whining, pining thing! An hour before he died, he bound me by vow to keep the creature. I would as soon have been charged with a pauper brat of a workhouse; but he was weak, naturally weak. John does not at all resemble his father, and I'm glad of it. Oh, I wish he would cease tormenting me with letters for money! John gambles dreadfully, and always loses—poor boy!"

She was getting much excited.

"I think I had better leave her now," said I to Bessie, who stood on the other side of the bed.

"Perhaps you had, Miss: but she often talks in this way towards night—in the morning she is calmer."

Bessie now endeavored to persuade Mrs. Reed to take a sedative draught; soon after, she grew more composed, and sank into a dozing state. I then left her.

More than ten days elapsed before I had again any conversation with her. She continued either delirious or lethargic; and the doctor forbade everything which could painfully excite her. Meantime, I got on as well as I could with Georgiana and Eliza.

One wet and windy afternoon I bethought myself to go upstairs and see how the dying woman sped, who lay there almost unheeded: the very servants paid her but a remittent attention, the hired nurse would slip out of the room whenever she could. I found the sickroom unwatched; the patient lay still; the fire was dying in the grate. I renewed the fuel, rearranged the bedclothes, and then moved away to the window.

The rain beat against the panes, the wind blew tempestuously. One lies there, I thought, who will soon be beyond the war of earthly elements. Whither will that spirit flit when at length released?

In pondering the great mystery, I thought of Helen Burns: recalled her dying words—her faith in the equality of disembodied souls. I was still listening in thought to her well-remembered tones when a feeble voice murmured from the couch behind:

"Who is that?"

I knew Mrs. Reed had not spoken for days; was she reviving? I went up to her.

"It is I, Aunt Reed."

"Who—I?" was her answer. "Who are you?" looking at me with a sort of alarm. "Who calls me aunt? You are not one of the Gibsons; and yet I know you—why, you are like Jane Eyre!"

I said nothing: I was afraid of occasioning some shock.

"Yet," said she, "I am afraid it is a mistake. I wished to see Jane Eyre, and I fancy a likeness where none exists; besides, in more than eight years she must be so changed."

Seeing that her senses were quite collected, I now gently

assured her that I was the person she supposed me to be. "I am very ill, I know," she said ere long. "It is as well I should ease my mind before I die. Is the nurse here? Or is there no one in the room but you?"

I assured her we were alone.

"Well, I have twice done you a wrong which I regret now. One was in breaking the promise which I gave my husband to bring you up as my own child; the other—" She stopped. "After all, it is of no great importance, perhaps," she murmured to herself; "and then I may get better; and to humble myself so to her is painful."

She made an effort to alter her position, but failed; her face changed; she seemed to experience some inward sensation—the precursor, perhaps, of the last pang.

"Well, I must get it over. Eternity is before me: I had better tell her. Go to my dressing case, and take out a letter you will see there."

I obeyed her directions. "Read the letter," she said. It was short, and thus conceived:

Madam,
    Will you have the goodness to send me the address of my niece, Jane Eyre, and to tell me how she is; it is my intention to write shortly and desire her to come to me at Madeira. Providence has blessed my endeavors to secure a competency; and as I am unmarried and childless, I wish to adopt her during my life, and bequeath her at my death whatever I may have to leave.
                                        I am, Madam, etc., etc.,
                                            JOHN EYRE, Madeira

It was dated three years back.

"Why did I never hear of this?" I asked.

"Because I disliked you too thoroughly ever to lend a hand in lifting you to prosperity. I could not forget your conduct to me, Jane—the fury with which you once turned on me. Bring me some water! Oh, make haste!"

"Dear Mrs. Reed," said I, as I offered her the draught she required, "think no more of all this, let it pass away from your mind. Forgive me for my passionate language; I was a child then."

She heeded nothing of what I said; but when she had tasted the water and drawn breath, she went on thus:

"I tell you I could not forget it; and I took my revenge. I wrote to your uncle; I said I was sorry, but Jane Eyre had died of typhus fever at Lowood. Now act as you please: write and contradict my assertion—expose my falsehood as soon as you like."

"If you could but be persuaded to think no more of it, Aunt, and to regard me with kindness and forgiveness—"

"You have a very bad disposition," said she, "and one to this day I feel it impossible to understand."

"My disposition is not so bad as you think. Many a time, as a little child, I should have been glad to love you if you would have let me; and I long earnestly to be reconciled to you now. Kiss me, Aunt." I approached my cheek to her lips; she would not touch it. "Love me, then, or hate me, as you will," I said at last, "you have my full and free forgiveness. Ask now for God's; and be at peace."

Poor, suffering woman! It was too late for her to make now the effort to change her habitual frame of mind: living, she had ever hated me—dying, she must hate me still.

The nurse now entered; I yet lingered half an hour longer, hoping to see some sign of amity, but she gave none. She was fast relapsing into stupor; nor did her mind again rally. At twelve o'clock that night she died.

CHAPTER X

MR. ROCHESTER HAD GIVEN ME but one week's leave of absence, yet a month elapsed before I quitted Gateshead. I wished to leave immediately after the funeral; but Georgiana entreated me to stay till she could get off to London, whither she was now at last invited by her uncle, Mr. Gibson. At last I saw Georgiana off; but now it was Eliza's turn to request me to stay another week. She was about to take the veil in a nunnery on the Continent—a vocation, I thought, which would suit her to a hair; and her plans required all her time and attention, she said. She wished me to look after the house, and to see callers.

At last, however, she told me I was at liberty, and I took my leave. The journey seemed tedious—very tedious. I was going back to Thornfield, but how long was I to stay there? Not long, of that I was sure. I had heard from Mrs. Fairfax in my absence. The party at the hall was dispersed; Mr. Rochester had left for London three weeks ago, but he was then expected to return in a fortnight. Mrs. Fairfax surmised that he was gone to make arrangements for his wedding, as he had talked of purchasing a new carriage; she said the idea of his marrying Miss Ingram seemed strange to her; but from what everybody said, she could no longer doubt that the event would shortly take place.

I had not notified Mrs. Fairfax the exact day of my return, for I did not wish to be met at Millcote. I proposed to walk the distance by myself; and very quietly, after leaving my box in the ostler's care, did I slip away from the George Inn, about six o'clock of a June evening, and take the road to Thornfield.

It was not a bright or splendid summer evening, though fair and soft; the haymakers were at work all along the road; and the sky, though far from cloudless, was such as promised well for the future. I felt glad as the road shortened before me; so glad that I stopped once to ask myself what that joy meant, and to remind Reason that it was not to my home I was going, or to a place where fond friends looked out for me and waited my arrival. "Mrs. Fairfax will smile you a calm welcome, to be sure," said I; "and little Adèle will clap her hands and jump to see you; but you know very well you are thinking of another than they; and that he is not thinking of you."

But what is so headstrong as youth? What so blind as inexperience? These affirmed that it was pleasure enough to have the privilege of again looking on Mr. Rochester, whether he looked on me or not; and they added—"Hasten! Be with him while you may; but a few more days or weeks at most, and you are parted with him forever!"

They are making hay, too, in Thornfield meadows; or rather, the laborers are just quitting their work, and returning home with their rakes on their shoulders, now, at the hour I arrive. I have but a field or two to traverse, and then I shall reach the gates. How full the hedges are of roses! I passed a tall brier, shooting leafy and flowery branches across the path; I see the narrow stile with stone steps; and I see—Mr. Rochester sitting there, a book and a pencil in his hand; he is writing.

Well, he is not a ghost; yet every nerve I have is unstrung. What does it mean? I did not think I should tremble in this way when I saw him—or lose the power of motion in his presence. I will go back as soon as I can stir: I need not make an absolute fool of myself. I know another way to the house. It does not signify if I knew twenty ways, for he has seen me.

"Hillo!" he cries, and he puts up his book and his pencil. "There you are! Come on, if you please."

I suppose I do come on; though in what fashion I know not, being scarcely cognizant of my movements, and solicitous only to appear calm, and, above all, to control the muscles of my face.

"And this is Jane Eyre? Are you coming from Millcote on foot? Yes—just one of your tricks: not to send for a carriage, but to steal to your home along with twilight, just as if you were a shade. What the deuce have you done with yourself this last month?"

"I have been with my aunt, sir, who is dead."

"A true Janian reply! Angels be my guard! She comes from the other world—from the abode of people who are dead; and tells me so when she meets in the gloaming! Truant!" he added, when he had paused an instant. "Absent from me a whole month, and forgetting me quite, I'll be sworn!"

I knew there would be pleasure in meeting my master again, even though broken by the fear that he was so soon to cease to be my master, and by the knowledge that I was nothing to him; but there was ever in Mr. Rochester such a wealth of the power of communicating happiness that to taste but of the crumbs he scattered to stray birds like me was to feast genially. His last words were balm: they seemed to imply that it imported something to him whether I forgot him or not. And he had spoken of Thornfield as my home—would that it were my home!

He did not leave the stile, and I hardly liked to ask to go by. I inquired soon if he had not been to London.

"Yes; I suppose you found that out by second sight?"

"Mrs. Fairfax told me in a letter."

"And did she inform you what I went to do?"

"Oh, yes, sir! Everybody knew your errand."

"You must see the carriage, Jane, and tell me if you don't think it will suit Mrs. Rochester exactly; and whether she won't look like Queen Boadicea, leaning back against those purple cushions. I wish, Jane, I were a trifle better adapted to match with her externally. Tell me, now, fairy as you are, can't you give me a charm or a philter to make me a handsome man?"

"It would be past the power of magic, sir," and, in thought, I added, A loving eye is all the charm needed; to such you are handsome enough, or rather, your sternness has a power beyond beauty.

Mr. Rochester had sometimes read my unspoken thoughts with an acumen to me incomprehensible. In the present instance he took no notice of my abrupt vocal response, but he smiled at me with a certain smile which he used but on rare occasions. It was the real sunshine of feeling—he shed it over me now.

"Pass, Janet," said he, making room for me to cross the stile; "go up home, and stay your weary little wandering feet at a friend's threshold."

All I had now to do was to obey him in silence. I got over the stile without a word, and meant to leave him calmly. An impulse held me fast—a force turned me round. I said—or something in me said in spite of me:

"Thank you, Mr. Rochester, for your great kindness. I am strangely glad to get back again to you, and wherever you are is my home—my only home."

I walked on so fast that even he could hardly have overtaken me. Little Adèle was wild with delight when she saw me. Mrs. Fairfax received me with her usual friendliness. This was very pleasant:

there is no happiness like that of being loved by your fellow creatures, and feeling that your presence adds to their comfort.

A fortnight of dubious calm succeeded my return to Thornfield Hall. Nothing was said of the master's marriage, and I saw no preparation going on for such an event. Almost every day I asked Mrs. Fairfax if she had yet heard anything decided; her answer was always in the negative. Once, she said, she had actually put the question to Mr. Rochester, but he had answered her only by a joke, and one of his queer looks, and she could not tell what to make of him.

One thing specially surprised me, and that was, there were no journeyings backward and forward, no visits to Ingram Park. To be sure it was twenty miles off, but what was that distance to an ardent lover? I began to cherish hopes I had no right to conceive: that the match was broken off; that one or both parties had changed their minds. I used to look at my master's face to see if it were sad or fierce, but I could not remember the time when it had been so uniformly clear of clouds. If, in the moments my pupil and I spent with him, I sank into dejection, he became even gay. Never had he called me more frequently to his presence, never been kinder to me when there—and, alas! never had I loved him so well.

CHAPTER XI

A SPLENDID MIDSUMMER SHONE over England: skies so pure, suns so radiant as were then seen in long succession seldom favor our wave-girt land. On Midsummer Eve, Adèle, weary with gathering wild strawberries in Hay Lane half the day, had gone to bed with the sun. I watched her drop asleep, and when I left her I sought the garden.

It was now the sweetest hour of the twenty-four, and dew fell cool on scorched plain and summit. The east had its own charm of fine, deep blue, and its own modest gem, a rising and solitary star; soon it would boast the moon, but she was yet beneath the horizon.

I walked awhile on the pavement, but a subtle, well-known scent—that of a cigar—stole from some window. I saw the library casement open a handbreadth; I knew I might be watched thence, so I went apart into the orchard. No nook in the grounds was more sheltered and more Edenlike; it was full of trees, it bloomed with flowers; a high wall shut it out from the court. At its bottom a sunk fence separated it from lonely fields, and a winding walk, terminating in a giant horse chestnut with a seat at its base, led down to the fence. Here one could wander unseen, and I felt as if I could haunt such shade forever; but in threading the flower and fruit parterres at the upper part of the enclosure, my step is stayed once more by a warning fragrance. I know it well—it is Mr. Rochester's cigar. I look round and I listen. I see trees laden with fruit, I hear a nightingale warbling; no coming step is audible, but that perfume increases; I must flee. I make for the wicket leading to the shrubbery, and I see Mr. Rochester entering. I step aside into the ivy recess; he will not stay long; if I sit still he will never see me.

But no—eventide is as pleasant to him as to me, and he strolls on, now lifting the gooseberry branches to look at the fruit, now stooping towards a knot of flowers. A great moth alights on a plant at his foot; he sees it, and bends to examine it.

Now, he has his back towards me, thought I; perhaps, if I walk softly, I can slip away unnoticed. But as I crossed his shadow, he said quietly without turning:

"Jane, come and look at this fellow."

I had made no noise, he had not eyes behind—could his shadow feel? I started at first, and then I approached him.

"Look at his wings," said he; "he reminds me of a West Indian insect. One does not often see so large and gay a night-rover in England. There! He is flown."

The moth roamed away. I was sheepishly retreating also, but Mr. Rochester followed me, and when we reached the wicket, he said, "Turn back; on so lovely a night it is a shame to sit in the house, and surely no one can wish to go to bed while sunset is thus at meeting with moonrise."

It is one of my faults, that though my tongue is sometimes

prompt enough at an answer, there are times when it sadly fails me in framing an excuse. I did not like to walk at this hour alone with Mr. Rochester in the shadowy orchard, but I could not find a reason to allege for leaving him.

"Jane," he recommenced, as we slowly strayed down in the direction of the sunk fence and the horse chestnut, "Thornfield is a pleasant place in summer, is it not?"

"Yes, sir."

"You must have become in some degree attached to the house?"

"I am attached to it, indeed."

"And I perceive you have acquired a degree of regard for that foolish little child Adèle, too, and even for simple Dame Fairfax?"

"Yes, sir; in different ways, I have an affection for both."

"And would be sorry to part with them?"

"Yes."

"Pity!" he said, and sighed. "It is always the way of events in this life," he continued presently. "No sooner have you got settled in a pleasant resting-place, than a voice calls out to you to rise and move on."

"Must I move on, sir?" I asked. "Must I leave Thornfield?"

"I believe you must, Jane. I am sorry, Janet, but I believe indeed you must."

This was a blow, but I did not let it prostrate me.

"Then you are going to be married, sir?"

"Ex-act-ly—pre-cise-ly. With your usual acuteness, you have hit the nail straight on the head."

"Soon, sir?"

"Very soon, my—that is, Miss Eyre; and you'll remember, Jane, the first time I, or Rumor, plainly intimated to you that it was my intention to put my old bachelor's neck into the sacred noose—to take Miss Ingram to my bosom, in short (she's an extensive armful, but one can't have too much of such a very excellent thing as my beautiful Blanche); well, as I was saying—listen to me, Jane! I wish to remind you that it was you who first said to me, with that discretion I respect in you, that in case I married Miss Ingram both you and little Adèle had better trot forthwith."

"Yes, sir, I will advertise immediately; meantime, I suppose"—
I was going to say, "I suppose I may stay here, till I find another
shelter," but I stopped, feeling it would not do to risk a long
sentence, for my voice was not quite under command.

"In about a month I hope to be a bridegroom," continued Mr.
Rochester, "and in the interim I shall myself look out for employment for you."

"Thank you, sir, I am sorry to give—"

"Oh, no need to apologize! I consider that when a dependent
does her duty as well as you have done yours, she has a sort of
claim upon her employer for any little assistance he can render her.
Indeed, I have already heard of a place that I think will suit: it is to
undertake the education of the five daughters of Mrs. Dionysius
O'Gall of Bitternutt Lodge, Connaught, Ireland. You'll like
Ireland, I think."

"It is a long way off, sir."

"No matter—a girl of your sense will not object to the voyage
or the distance."

"Not the voyage, but the distance; and the sea is a barrier—"

"From what, Jane?"

"From England and from Thornfield, and—"

"Well?"

"From *you*, sir."

I said this almost involuntarily, and my tears gushed out. I did
not cry so as to be heard, however; I avoided sobbing. The thought
of Mrs. O'Gall and Bitternutt Lodge struck cold to my heart.

"When you get to Ireland I shall never see you again, Jane; that's
morally certain. We have been good friends, Jane, have we not?"

"Yes, sir."

"And when friends are on the eve of separation, they like to
spend the little time that remains close to each other. Come—we'll
talk over the parting quietly, while the stars enter into their shining
life. Here is the chestnut, here is the bench at its roots. Come,
we will sit there tonight, though we should never more be destined to sit there together." He seated me and himself.

"It is a long way to Ireland, Janet, and I am sorry to send my little friend on such weary travels, but how is it to be helped? Are you anything akin to me, do you think, Jane?"

I could risk no sort of answer by this time: my heart was full.

"Because," he said, "I sometimes have a queer feeling with regard to you: it is as if I had a string somewhere under my left ribs, tightly and inextricably knotted to a similar string situated in the corresponding quarter of your little frame. And if that boisterous channel, and two hundred miles or so of land come broad between us, I am afraid that cord of communion will be snapped; and then I've a nervous notion I should take to bleeding inwardly. As for you—you'd forget me."

"That I *never* should, sir, you know—" Impossible to proceed.

"Jane, do you hear that nightingale singing in the wood? Listen!"

In listening, I sobbed convulsively, for I could repress what I endured no longer. The vehemence of emotion, stirred by grief and love within me, was claiming mastery. I spoke at last, and expressed an impetuous wish that I had never been born, or never come to Thornfield.

"Because you are sorry to leave it?"

"Yes. I grieve to leave Thornfield. I love Thornfield. I love it because I have lived in it a full and delightful life—momentarily at least. I have known you, Mr. Rochester; and it strikes me with terror and anguish to feel I must be torn from you forever. I see the necessity of departure, and it is like looking on the necessity of death."

"Where do you see the necessity?" he asked, suddenly.

"Where? You, sir, have placed it before me in the shape of Miss Ingram; a noble and beautiful woman—your bride."

"What bride? I have no bride!"

"But you will have."

"Yes, I will!—I will!" He set his teeth.

"Then I must go; you have said it yourself."

"No, you must stay! I swear it—and the oath shall be kept."

"I tell you I must go!" I retorted, roused to something like passion. "Do you think I can stay to become nothing to you? Do you think I am a machine without feelings? Do you think, because I am poor, obscure and plain, I am soulless and heartless? You think wrong! I have as much soul as you—and full as much heart! And if God had gifted me with some beauty, and much wealth, I should have made it as hard for you to leave me as it is now for me to leave you. I am not talking to you now through the medium of conventionalities, or even of mortal flesh: it is my spirit that addresses your spirit, just as if we stood at God's feet, equal—as we are!"

"As we are!" repeated Mr. Rochester. "So," he added, enclosing me in his arms, gathering me to his breast, pressing his lips on my lips; "so, Jane!"

"Yes, so, sir," I rejoined, "and yet not so; for you are a married man—or as good as a married man, and wed to one with whom you have no sympathy—whom I do not believe you truly love. I would scorn such a union; therefore I am better than you—let me go!"

"Where, Jane? To Ireland?"

"Yes—to Ireland."

"Jane, be still; don't struggle so, like a wild, frantic bird that rends its own plumage in its desperation."

"I am no bird, and no net ensnares me; I am a free human being with an independent will."

Another effort set me at liberty, and I stood erect before him.

"And your will shall decide your destiny," he said. "I offer you my hand, my heart, and a share of all my possessions."

"You play a farce, which I merely laugh at."

"I ask you to pass through life at my side—to be my second self and best earthly companion."

"For that fate you have already made your choice."

"Jane, be still a few moments; you are overexcited. I will be still too."

A waft of wind came sweeping down the laurel walk and trembled through the boughs of the chestnut; it wandered away—away—it died. The nightingale's song was then the only voice of the hour; in listening to it, I again wept. Mr. Rochester sat quiet, looking at me gently and seriously. Some time passed before he spoke; he at last said, "Come to my side, Jane, and let us understand one another."

"I will never again come to your side; I am torn away now, and cannot return."

"But, Jane, I summon you as my wife; it is you only I intend to marry."

I thought he mocked me. "Your bride stands between us," I said.

He rose, and with a stride reached me.

"My bride is here," he said, again drawing me to him, "because my equal is here, and my likeness. Jane, will you marry me?"

Still I did not answer, for I was still incredulous.

"Do you doubt me, Jane?"

"Entirely."

"Am I a liar in your eyes?" he asked passionately. "What love have I for Miss Ingram? None; and that you know. What love has she for me? None; as I have taken pains to prove. I caused a rumor to reach her that my fortune was not a third of what was supposed, and after that I presented myself to see the result; it was coldness both from her and her mother. I could not marry Miss Ingram. You—you strange—you almost unearthly thing—I love as my own flesh! You—poor and obscure, and small and plain as you are—I entreat to accept me as a husband."

"What, me!" I ejaculated, beginning in his earnestness—and especially in his incivility—to credit his sincerity. "Me who have not a friend in the world but you, not a shilling but what you have given me?"

"You, Jane. I must have you for my own—entirely my own. Will you be mine? Say yes, quickly."

"Mr. Rochester, turn to the moonlight. I want to read your countenance. Turn!"

"There. You will find it scarcely more legible than a crumpled, scratched page. Read on; only make haste, for I suffer."

His face was very much agitated, and there were strange gleams in the eyes. "Oh, Jane, you torture me!" he exclaimed. "With that searching and yet generous look you torture me!"

"How can I do that? If you are true and your offer real, my only feelings to you must be gratitude and devotion."

"Gratitude!" he ejaculated, and added wildly—"Jane, accept me. Say 'Edward'—give me my name—'Edward, I will marry you.' "

"Are you in earnest? Do you truly love me? Do you sincerely wish me to be your wife?"

"I do, and if an oath is necessary to satisfy you, I swear it."

"Then, sir, I will marry you."

"Call me Edward—my little wife!"

"Dear Edward!"

"Come to me—come to me entirely now," said he; and added in his deepest tone, speaking in my ear as his cheek was laid on mine, "Make my happiness—I will make yours.

"God pardon me!" he subjoined ere long. "And man meddle not with me; I have her, and will hold her."

"There is no one to meddle, sir. I have no kindred to interfere."

"No—that is the best of it," he said. Then again and again he said, "Are you happy, Jane?" and again and again I answered, "Yes." After which he murmured, "It will atone—it will atone. Have I not found her friendless, cold and comfortless? Will I not guard, cherish and solace her? I know my Maker sanctions what I do. For man's opinion—I defy it."

But what had befallen the night? The moon was not yet set, and we were all in shadow: I could scarcely see my master's face, near as I was. And what ailed the chestnut tree? It writhed and groaned, while wind roared in the laurel walk, and came sweeping over us.

"We must go in," said Mr. Rochester; "the weather changes. I could have sat with thee till morning, Jane."

And so, thought I, could I with you.

The rain rushed down. Mr. Rochester hurried me up the walk, and into the house. He was taking off my shawl in the hall, when Mrs. Fairfax emerged from her room. I did not observe her at first, nor did Mr. Rochester. The lamp was lit. The clock was on the stroke of twelve.

"Hasten to take off your wet things," said he, "and before you go, good night—good night, my darling!"

He kissed me repeatedly. When I looked up, on leaving his arms, there stood the widow, pale, grave and amazed. I only smiled at her, and ran upstairs. Explanation will do for another time, thought I. Still, when I reached my chamber, I felt a pang at the idea she should even temporarily misconstrue what she had seen.

But joy soon effaced every other feeling; and loud as the wind blew, near and deep as the thunder crashed, fierce and frequent as the lightning gleamed, I experienced no fear. Mr. Rochester came thrice to my door in the course of it, to ask if I was safe and tranquil, and that was comfort, that was strength for anything.

Before I left my bed in the morning, little Adèle came running in to tell me that the great horse chestnut at the bottom of the orchard had been struck by lightning in the night, and half of it split away.

As I ROSE AND DRESSED, I thought over what had happened, and wondered if it were a dream. I could not be certain of the reality till I had seen Mr. Rochester again, and heard him renew his words of love. Still my mood was blissful. I was not surprised, when I ran down into the hall, to see that a brilliant June morning had succeeded to the tempest of the night, and to feel, through the open door, the breathing of a fresh and fragrant breeze. Nature must be gladsome when I was so happy.

Mrs. Fairfax surprised me by looking out of the window with a sad countenance, and saying gravely, "Miss Eyre, will you come to breakfast?" During the meal she was quiet and cool; but I must wait for my master to give explanations, and so must she. I ate, and then I hastened upstairs. I met Adèle leaving the schoolroom.

"Where are you going? It is time for lessons."

"Mr. Rochester has sent me away to the nursery."

"Where is he?"

"In there," pointing to the apartment she had left, and I went in, and there he stood.

"Come and bid me good morning," said he.

I gladly advanced, and it was not merely a cold word now, or even a shake of the hand that I received, but an embrace and a kiss. It seemed natural, it seemed genial to be so well loved, so caressed by him.

"Jane, you look blooming, and smiling, and pretty," said he; "truly pretty this morning. Is this my pale little elf? This little sunny-faced girl with the dimpled cheek and rosy lips, the satin-smooth hazel hair, and the radiant hazel eyes?"

"It is Jane Eyre, sir."

"Soon to be Jane Rochester," he added. "In four weeks, Janet, not a day more. Do you hear that?"

I did, and I could not quite comprehend it; it made me giddy.

"You blushed, and now you are white, Jane; what is that for?"

"Because you gave me a new name—Jane Rochester; and it seems so strange."

"Yes, Mrs. Rochester," said he; "young Mrs. Rochester—Fairfax Rochester's girl bride."

"It can never be, sir; it does not sound likely. To imagine such a lot befalling me is a fairy tale—a daydream."

"Which I can and will realize. I shall begin today. This morning I wrote to my banker in London to send me certain jewels he has in his keeping—heirlooms for the ladies of Thornfield. In a day or two I hope to pour them into your lap."

"Oh, sir, never mind jewels! I would rather not have them."

"I will myself put the diamond chain round your neck, and the circlet on your forehead, which it will become; for nature has stamped her patent of nobility on this brow, Jane."

"No, no, sir! Don't address me as if I were a beauty; I am your plain, Quakerish governess."

"You are a beauty, in my eyes, and I will make the world acknowledge you a beauty, too. I will attire my Jane in satin and lace, and she shall have roses in her hair."

"And then you won't know me, sir, and I shall not be your Jane Eyre any longer, but a jay in borrowed plumes. Sir, I don't call you handsome, though I love you most dearly; far too dearly to flatter you. Don't flatter me."

He pursued his theme, however, without noticing my deprecation. "This very day I shall take you in the carriage to Millcote, and you must choose some dresses for yourself. I told you we shall be married in four weeks. The wedding is to take place quietly, in the church down yonder, near our gate; and then I shall waft you away at once to town. After a brief stay there, I shall bear my treasure to regions nearer the sun—to French vineyards and Italian plains."

"Shall I travel—and with you, sir?"

"You shall sojourn at Paris, Rome and Naples; at Florence, Venice and Vienna: all the ground I have wandered over shall be retrodden by you. Ten years since, I flew through Europe half mad; now I shall revisit it healed and cleansed, with a very angel as my comforter."

I laughed at him as he said this. "I am not an angel," I asserted; "and I will not be one till I die—I will be myself. Mr. Rochester, you must neither expect nor exact anything celestial of me—for you will not get it, any more than I shall get it of you."

"What do you anticipate of me?"

"For a little while you will perhaps be as you are now, and then you will be capricious; and then you will be stern, and I shall have much ado to please you. But when you get well used to me, you will perhaps like me again—*like* me, I say, not *love* me. I suppose your love will effervesce in six months, or less. Yet, after all, as a friend and companion, I hope never to become quite distasteful to my dear master."

"Distasteful! And like you again! I think I shall like you again and yet again, and I will make you confess I do not only *like*, but *love* you—with truth, fervor, constancy."

"I wonder how you will answer me a year hence, should I ask a favor it does not suit your convenience or pleasure to grant."

"Ask me something now, Janet—the least thing; I desire to be entreated—"

"Indeed, I will, sir; I have my petition all ready."

"Speak! But if you look up and smile with that countenance, I shall swear concession before I know to what, and that will make a fool of me."

"Not at all, sir; I ask only this: don't send for the jewels, and don't crown me with roses; you might as well put a border of gold lace round that plain pocket handkerchief you have there."

"I might as well 'gild refined gold.' I know it: your request is granted then—for the time. I will remand the order I dispatched to my banker. But you have not yet asked for anything; try again."

"Well, then, sir, have the goodness to gratify my curiosity; which is much piqued on one point."

He looked disturbed. "What? What?" he said hastily. "Curiosity is a dangerous petition."

"But there can be no danger in complying with this, sir. This is what I have to ask. Why did you take such pains to make me believe you wished to marry Miss Ingram?"

"Is that all! Thank God, it is no worse!" And now he unknit his brows, smiled, and stroked my hair. "I think I may confess," he continued, "even although I should make you a little indignant, Jane—well, I feigned courtship of Miss Ingram because I wished to render you as madly in love with me as I was with you, and I knew jealousy would be the best ally I could call in."

"Excellent! Now you are small—not one whit bigger than the end of my little finger. It was a scandalous disgrace to act in that way. Did you think nothing of Miss Ingram's feelings, sir?"

"Her feelings are concentrated in one—pride; and I told you how the idea of my insolvency extinguished her flame in a moment."

"Then may I enjoy the great good that has been vouchsafed to me without fearing that anyone else is suffering?"

"That you may, my good little girl."

I turned my lips to the hand that lay on my shoulder. I loved him very much—more than I could trust myself to say—more than words had power to express.

"Ask something more," he said presently; "it is my delight to be entreated."

I was again ready with my request. "Communicate your intentions to Mrs. Fairfax, sir; she saw me with you last night, and she was shocked. It pains me to be misjudged by so good a woman."

"Go to your room, and put on your bonnet," he replied. "I mean you to accompany me to Millcote this morning, and while you prepare for the drive, I will enlighten the old lady."

I was soon dressed; and when I heard Mr. Rochester quit Mrs. Fairfax's parlor, I hurried down to it. The old lady had been reading her morning portion of Scripture; her Bible lay open before her. Her eyes expressed the surprise of a quiet mind stirred by unwonted tidings. Seeing me, she roused herself; she made a sort of effort to smile, and framed a few words of congratulation, but the sentence was abandoned unfinished.

"I feel so astonished," she began, "I hardly know what to say to you, Miss Eyre. I have surely not been dreaming, have I? Now, can you tell me whether it is actually true that Mr. Rochester has asked you to marry him?"

"Yes."

She looked at me bewildered. "I could never have thought it. He is a proud man—all the Rochesters were proud—and his father, at least, liked money. He means to marry you?"

"He tells me so."

She surveyed my whole person "It passes me," she continued, "but no doubt it is true since you say so. How it will answer, I cannot tell. Equality of position and fortune is often advisable in such cases; and there are twenty years of difference in your ages. Is it really for love he is going to marry you?" she asked.

I was so hurt by her coldness and skepticism that the tears rose to my eyes. "Why, am I a monster?" I said. "Is it impossible that Mr. Rochester should have a sincere affection for me?"

"No: you are very well, and I have always noticed that you were a sort of pet of Mr. Rochester's. There are times when, for your sake, I have been a little uneasy at his marked preference; last night I cannot tell you what I suffered when I sought all over the house, and could find you nowhere, nor the master either; and then, at twelve o'clock, saw you come in with him."

"Well, never mind that now," I interrupted; "it is enough that all was right."

"I hope all will be right in the end," she said; "but, believe me, you cannot be too careful. Try and keep Mr. Rochester at a distance; distrust yourself as well as him. Gentlemen in his station are not accustomed to marry their governesses."

I was growing truly irritated; happily, Adèle ran in.

"Let me go—let me go to Millcote too!" she cried. "Mr. Rochester won't, though there is so much room in the new carriage. Beg him to let me go, Mademoiselle."

"That I will, Adèle"; and I hastened away with her. The carriage was ready, and my master was pacing the pavement, Pilot following him backwards and forwards. "Adèle may accompany us, may she not, sir?"

"I told her no. I'll have only you."

"Do let her go, Mr. Rochester, please; it would be better."

"Not it: she will be a restraint."

He was quite peremptory, both in look and voice. The chill of Mrs. Fairfax's warning was upon me: something of uncertainty had beset my hopes. I was about mechanically to obey him, but as he helped me into the carriage, he looked at my face.

"What is the matter?" he asked. "All the sunshine is gone. Do you really wish the bairn to go?"

"I would far rather she went, sir."

"Then off for your bonnet, and back, like a flash of lightning!" cried he to Adèle.

She obeyed him with what speed she might.

"After all, a single morning's interruption will not matter much," said he, "when I mean shortly to claim you—your thoughts, conversation and company—for life."

CHAPTER XII

THE MONTH OF COURTSHIP had wasted; its very last hours were being numbered. All preparations for the bridal day were complete. *I*, at least, had nothing more to do: I had even written to my newly found Uncle John Eyre, in Madeira, to tell him I was going to be married, and to whom. My trunks were packed and ranged in a row along the wall of my little chamber; tomorrow, at this time, they would be far on their road to London, and so should I—or rather, not I, but one Jane Rochester, a person whom as yet I knew not. She would not be born till tomorrow, some time after eight o'clock a.m.

In the meantime, in yonder closet garments said to be hers had displaced my black stuff Lowood frock and straw bonnet; there also hung in yonder closet a suit of wedding raiment—a pearl-colored robe, a vapory veil. I shut the closet, to conceal the strange, wraithlike apparel it contained, which, at this evening hour—nine o'clock—gave out certainly a most ghostly shimmer through the shadow of my apartment.

"I will leave you by yourself, white dream," I said. "I am feverish. I heard the wind blowing; I will go out-of-doors and feel it."

It was not only the hurry of preparation that made me feverish; not only the anticipation of the new life which was to commence tomorrow; both these circumstances had their share in producing that restless mood which hurried me forth at this late hour into the darkening grounds. But a third cause influenced my mind more than they.

I had at heart a strange and anxious thought. Something had happened which I could not comprehend; no one knew of the event but myself; it had taken place the preceding night. Mr. Rochester had been absent from home; nor was he yet returned. Business had called him to a small estate he possessed thirty miles off— business it was requisite he should settle in person, previous to his departure from England. I waited now his return, eager to seek of him the solution to the enigma that perplexed me.

I sought the orchard, driven to its shelter by the wind, which all day had blown strong and full from the south. Instead of subsiding as night drew on, it seemed to augment its rush and deepen its roar: the trees blew steadfastly one way, scarcely tossing back their boughs once in an hour; the clouds drifted from pole to pole, fast following, mass on mass. Running before the wind, I descended the laurel walk, then faced the wreck of the chestnut tree. It stood up, black and riven; the trunk, split down the center, gaped ghastly. The cloven halves were not broken from each other, for the firm base and strong roots kept them unsundered below; though community of vitality was destroyed and the sap could flow no more, as yet, however, they could be said to form one tree—a ruin, but an entire ruin.

"You did right to hold fast to each other," I said, as if the monster splinters were living things, and could hear me. "I think, scathed as you look, you are not desolate: each of you has a comrade to sympathize with him in his decay." As I looked up at them, the moon appeared momentarily in that part of the sky which filled their fissure; her disk was blood-red and half overcast; then she buried herself again in cloud. The wind fell, for a second, round Thornfield, but far away over wood and water poured a wild, melancholy wail. It was sad to listen to, and I ran off again, back to the house. The old clock in the hall simultaneously struck ten.

"How late it grows!" I said, and I was seized with hypochondriac foreboding. "I will run down to the gates and onto the road. It is

moonlight at intervals; I can see a good way. He may be coming now, and to meet him will save some minutes of suspense."

I set out. The wind roared high in the great trees which embowered the gates; I walked past them. But ere I had measured a quarter of a mile, I heard the tramp of hoofs; a horseman came on, full gallop; a dog ran by his side. It was he, mounted on Mesrour, followed by Pilot. He saw me, for the moon once again rode watery bright in the sky. He took his hat off, and waved it round his head. I now ran to meet him.

"There!" he exclaimed, as he stretched out his hand and bent from the saddle. "You can't do without me, that is evident. Step on my boot toe; give me both hands; mount!"

I obeyed; joy made me agile: I sprang up before him. A hearty kissing I got for a welcome, and some boastful triumph, which I swallowed as well as I could. He checked himself in his exultation to demand, "But is there anything the matter, Janet, that you come to meet me at such an hour?"

"No; but I thought you would never come. I could not bear to wait in the house for you, especially with this wind."

"Wind, indeed! Pull my cloak round you; but I think you are feverish, Jane: your cheek is burning hot. I ask again, is there anything the matter?"

"I'll tell you by and by, sir; and I daresay you will laugh at me for my pains."

"I'll laugh at you heartily when tomorrow is past; till then I dare not: my prize is not certain. This is you, who have been as slippery as an eel this last month, and as thorny as a brier rose. I could not lay a finger anywhere but I was pricked; and now I seem to have gathered up a stray lamb in my arms. You wandered out of the fold to seek your shepherd, did you, Jane?"

"I wanted you, but don't boast. Here we are at Thornfield; now let me down."

He landed me on the pavement. John took his horse, and he followed me into the library, where his supper was served.

"Take a seat and bear me company, Jane. Please God, it is the last meal but one you will eat at Thornfield Hall for a long time."

I sat down near him, but told him I could not eat.

"Is it the prospect of a journey that takes away your appetite, Jane?"

"I cannot see my prospects clearly tonight, sir. Everything in life seems unreal."

"Except me. I am substantial enough—touch me."

"You, sir, are the most phantomlike of all: you are a mere dream."

He held out his hand, laughing. "Is that a dream?" said he, placing it close to my eyes.

"Yes; though I touch it, it is a dream," said I, as I put it down from before my face. "Sir, have you finished supper?"

"Yes, Jane."

I rang the bell, and ordered away the tray. When we were again alone, I took a low seat at my master's knee.

"It is near midnight," I said.

"Yes; but remember, Jane, you promised to wake with me the night before my wedding."

"I did; and I will keep my promise, for an hour or two at least."

"Are all your arrangements complete?"

"All, sir."

"And on my part, likewise," he returned. "I have settled everything; and we leave Thornfield tomorrow, within half an hour after our return from church."

"Very well, sir."

"With what an extraordinary smile you uttered those words 'very well,' Jane! What a bright spot of color you have on each cheek! Are you well? Tell me what you feel."

"I could not, sir; no words could tell you what I feel."

"You puzzle me, Jane; your look perplexes and pains me. I want an explanation."

"Then, sir, listen. All day yesterday I was very busy, and very happy in my bustle; for I am not, as you seem to think, troubled by any fears; I think it a glorious thing to have the hope of living with you. No, sir, don't caress me now—let me talk undisturbed. Yesterday it was a fine day, if you recollect—the calmness of the air and sky forbade apprehensions regarding your safety on your journey. I walked a little while on the pavement after tea, thinking of you; I thought of the life that lay before me—*your* life, sir—an existence more expansive and stirring than my own. I wondered why moralists call this world a dreary wilderness; for me it blossomed like a rose.

"At sunset, I went in. Sophie called me upstairs to look at my wedding dress, which they had just brought; and under it in the box I found your present—the veil which, in your extravagance, you sent for from London. I smiled as I unfolded it, and devised how I would tease you about your efforts to masque your plebeian bride as a peeress. I thought how I would carry down to you the square of plain blonde lace I had myself prepared as a covering for my head, and ask if that was not good enough for a woman who could bring her husband neither fortune, beauty nor connections. I saw plainly how you would look; and heard your haughty disavowal of any necessity on your part to augment your wealth, or elevate your standing, by marrying either a purse or a coronet."

"How well you read me, you witch!" interposed Mr. Rochester; "but what did you find in the veil besides its embroidery? Did you find poison or a dagger that you look so mournful now?"

"No, no, sir; besides the delicacy and richness of the fabric, I found nothing save Fairfax Rochester's pride. But, sir, as it grew dark, the wind rose; it blew yesterday with a sullen, moaning sound. I wished you were at home. For some time after I went to bed I could not sleep—a sense of anxious excitement distressed me. On sleeping, I continued the wish to be with you, and experienced a strange, regretful consciousness of some barrier dividing us. During all my first sleep, I was following the windings of an unknown road; it was night time; I was burdened with the charge of a little child, too young and feeble to walk, which shivered in my cold arms, and wailed piteously in my ear. Then I dreamt, sir, that I came to Thornfield Hall, and that Thornfield Hall was a dreary ruin, the retreat of bats and owls. I thought that of all the stately front nothing remained but a shell-like wall, high, fragile-looking. I wandered, by moonlight, through the grass-grown enclosure within; here I stumbled over a marble hearth, there over a fragment of cornice. I still carried the unknown child: I might not lay it down, however tired my arms. I heard a gallop of a horse at a distance on the road; I was sure it was you, and you were departing for many years, and for a distant country. I climbed the thin wall with frantic, perilous haste, eager to catch one last glimpse of you from the top. The stones rolled from under my feet, the ivy I grasped gave way; then the wall crumbled under me; I lost my balance, fell and woke."

"Now, Jane, that is all?"

"All the preface, sir; the tale is yet to come. On waking, a gleam dazzled my eyes. I thought, Oh, it is daylight! But it was only candlelight. Sophie, I supposed, had come in. There was a light on the dressing table, and the door of the closet, where I had hung my wedding dress and veil, stood open; I heard a rustling there. I asked, 'Sophie, what are you doing?' No one answered, but a form emerged from the closet; it took the light, held it aloft and surveyed the garments. 'Sophie!' I again cried, and still it was silent. I had risen up in bed. First surprise, then bewilderment, came over me; and then my blood crept cold through my veins. Mr. Rochester, this was not Sophie, it was not Leah, it was not Mrs. Fairfax. It was not even that strange woman, Grace Poole."

"It must have been one of them," interrupted my master.

"No, sir. The shape standing before me had never crossed my eyes before; the height, the contour, were new to me."

"Describe it, Jane."

"It seemed, sir, a woman, tall and large, with thick and dark hair hanging long down her back. Her dress was white and straight; but whether gown, sheet or shroud, I cannot tell."

"Did you see her face?"

"Not at first. But presently she took my veil; she gazed at it, then threw it over her head, and turned to the mirror. At that moment I saw the reflection of the visage and features quite distinctly in the glass. Fearful and ghastly they were—oh, sir, I never saw a face like it! It was a discolored and savage face. I wish I could forget the roll of the red eyes!"

"Ghosts are usually pale, Jane."

"This, sir, was purple; the lips were swelled and dark, the brow furrowed, the black eyebrows widely raised over the bloodshot eyes. It reminded me of the foul German specter—the Vampire."

"Ah! What did it do?"

"Sir, it removed my veil from its gaunt head, rent it in two parts, and flinging both on the floor, trampled on them."

"Afterwards?"

"It drew aside the window curtain and looked out; then, taking the candle, it retreated to the door. Just at my bedside the figure stopped; the fiery eye glared upon me. I was aware her lurid visage flamed over mine, and I lost consciousness; for the second time in my life I became insensible from terror."

"Who was with you when you revived?"

"No one, sir, but the broad day. I rose, bathed my head and face, drank a long draught of water; felt that though enfeebled I was not ill, and determined that to none but you would I impart this vision. Now, sir, tell me who and what that woman was?"

"The creature of an overstimulated brain; that is certain. I must be careful of you, my treasure; nerves like yours were not made for rough handling."

"Sir, depend upon it, my nerves were not in fault; the thing was real."

"And your previous dream: was it real too? Is Thornfield a ruin? When we are once united, there shall be no recurrence of these mental terrors, I guarantee that."

"Mental terrors, sir! I wish I could believe them to be only such, since even you cannot explain to me the mystery of that awful visitant."

"And since I cannot do it, Jane, it must have been unreal."

"But, sir, when I said so to myself on rising this morning, and when I looked round the room to gather courage and comfort from the cheerful aspect of each familiar object, there—on the carpet—I saw the veil, torn from top to bottom in two halves!"

I felt Mr. Rochester start and shudder; he hastily flung his arms round me. "Thank God," he exclaimed, "that if anything malignant did come near you last night, it was only the veil that was harmed. Oh, to think what might have happened!"

He drew his breath short, and strained me so close I could scarcely pant. After some minutes' silence, he continued, cheerily:

"Now, Janet, I'll explain to you all about it. It was half dream, half reality: a woman did, I doubt not, enter your room, and that woman was—must have been—Grace Poole. In a state between sleeping and waking, you noticed her entrance and her actions; but feverish as you were, you ascribed to her a goblin appearance different from her own. The spiteful tearing of the veil was real, and it is like her. I see you would ask why I keep such a woman in my house; when we have been married a year and a day, I will tell you, but not now. Are you satisfied, Jane? Do you accept my solution of the mystery?"

I reflected, and in truth it appeared to me the only possible one. Satisfied I was not, but to please him I endeavored to appear so; relieved I certainly did feel, so I answered him with a contented smile. And now, as it was past one, I prepared to leave him.

"Does not Sophie sleep with Adèle in the nursery?" he asked, as I lit my candle.

"Yes, sir."

"And there is room enough in Adèle's little bed for you. You must share it with her tonight, Jane."

"I shall be glad to do so, sir."

"And fasten the door on the inside. And now, no more somber thoughts: chase dull care away, Janet. Look here"—he walked to the library window and lifted up the curtain—"it is a lovely night!"

It was. Half heaven was now pure and stainless; the clouds were filing off eastward in long, silvered columns. The moon shone peacefully.

"Well," said Mr. Rochester, gazing into my eyes, "how is my Janet now?"

"The night is serene, sir, and so am I."

"And you will not dream of separation and sorrow tonight, but of happy love and blissful union."

This prediction was but half fulfilled: I did not indeed dream of sorrow, but as little did I dream of joy, for I never slept at all. With little Adèle in my arms, I watched the slumber of childhood—so tranquil, so innocent—and waited for the coming day; and as soon as the sun rose I rose too. I remember Adèle clung to me as I left her; I remember I kissed her; and I cried over her with strange emotion, and quitted her because I feared my sobs would break her still sound repose. She seemed the emblem of my past life; and he I was now to array myself to meet, the dread, but adored, type of my unknown future day.

CHAPTER XIII

Sophie came at seven to dress me; she was very long indeed in accomplishing her task; so long that Mr. Rochester sent up to ask why I did not come. She was just fastening my veil (the plain square of blonde lace after all) to my hair with a brooch. I hurried from under her hands as soon as I could.

"Stop!" she cried in French. "Look at yourself in the mirror, you have not taken one peep."

So I turned at the door. I saw a veiled figure, so unlike my usual self that it seemed almost the image of a stranger. "Jane!" called a voice, and I hastened down. I was received at the foot of the stairs by Mr. Rochester. "Lingerer," he said, "my brain is on fire with impatience; and you tarry so long!"

He took me into the dining room, surveyed me keenly all over, pronounced me "fair as a lily," and then telling me he would give me but ten minutes to eat some breakfast, he rang the bell. A footman answered it. "Is John getting the carriage ready?"

"Yes, sir."

"We shall not want it to go to church; but it must be ready the moment we return—all the luggage strapped on, and the coachman in his seat. Go you to the church; see if Mr. Wood [the clergyman] and the clerk are there; return and tell me."

The footman soon returned.

"Mr. Wood is in the vestry, sir, putting on his surplice."

"Jane, are you ready?"

I rose. There were no groomsmen, no bridesmaids to wait for: none but Mr. Rochester and I. Mrs. Fairfax stood in the hall as we passed. I would fain have spoken to her, but my hand was held by a grasp of iron. I was hurried along, and to look at Mr. Rochester's face was to feel that not a second of delay would be tolerated for any purpose.

At the churchyard he stopped; he discovered I was quite out of breath. "Am I cruel in my love?" he said. "Delay an instant; lean on me, Jane."

And now I can recall the picture of the gray old house of God rising calm before me. I have not forgotten, either, two figures of strangers, straying amongst the green grave mounds and reading the mementos on the few mossy headstones. I noticed them, because, as they saw us, they passed round the church; and I doubted not they were going to enter by the side-aisle door and witness the ceremony. By Mr. Rochester they were not observed; he was earnestly looking at my face, from which the blood had, I daresay, momentarily fled, for I felt my cheeks and lips cold. When I rallied, he walked gently with me up to the porch.

We entered the humble temple; the priest waited at the altar, the clerk beside him. All was still: two shadows only moved in a remote corner. Our place was taken at the communion rail. Hearing a cautious step behind me, I glanced over my shoulder; one of the strangers was advancing up the chancel. The service began. The explanation of the intent of matrimony was gone through; and then the clergyman came a step further forward, and went on:

"'I require and charge you both . . . that if either of you know any impediment, why ye may not lawfully be joined together in Matrimony, ye do now confess it. . . .'" He paused, as the custom is. When is that pause ever broken by reply? Not, perhaps, once in a hundred years. And the clergyman, who had not lifted his eyes from his book, and had held his breath but for a moment, was proceeding, when a distinct and near voice said:

"The marriage cannot go on; I declare the existence of an impediment."

The clergyman looked up at the speaker, and stood mute; the clerk did the same; Mr. Rochester moved slightly, as if an earthquake had rolled under his feet, and not turning his head or eyes, he said, "Proceed." Profound silence fell when he had uttered that word, with deep but low intonation. Presently Mr. Wood said, "I cannot proceed without some investigation into what has been asserted."

"The ceremony is quite broken off," subjoined the voice behind us. "An insuperable impediment to this marriage exists."

Mr. Rochester heard, but heeded not; he stood stubborn and rigid.

Mr. Wood seemed at a loss. "What is the nature of the impediment?" he asked. "Perhaps it may be got over?"

"Hardly," was the answer. "I have called it insuperable. It consists in the existence of a previous marriage. Mr. Rochester has a wife now living."

My nerves vibrated to those low-spoken words as they had

never vibrated to thunder—my blood felt their subtle violence as it had never felt frost or fire. I looked at Mr. Rochester; I made him look at me. His whole face was colorless rock; his eye was both spark and flint. He disavowed nothing; he seemed as if he would defy all things. Without speaking, without smiling, he only twined my waist with his arm, and riveted me to his side.

"Who are you?" he asked of the intruder.

"My name is Briggs—a solicitor of —— Street, London."

"And you would thrust on me a wife?"

"I would remind you of your lady's existence, sir."

"Favor me with an account of her—with her name, her parentage, her place of abode."

"Certainly." Mr. Briggs calmly took a paper from his pocket, and read out in a sort of official, nasal voice:

"'I affirm and can prove that on the 20th of October, A.D., —— [a date of fifteen years back], Edward Fairfax Rochester, of Thornfield Hall, in the county of ——, England, was married to my sister, Bertha Antoinetta Mason, daughter of Jonas Mason, merchant, and of Antoinetta his wife, a Creole, at —— church, Spanish Town, Jamaica. The record of the marriage will be found in the register of that church—a copy of it is now in my possession. Signed, Richard Mason.'"

"That—if a genuine document—may prove I have been married, but it does not prove that the woman mentioned as my wife is still living."

"She was living three months ago," returned the lawyer.

"How do you know?"

"I have a witness to the fact."

"Produce him—or go to hell."

"I will produce him first—he is on the spot; Mr. Mason, have the goodness to step forward."

Mr. Rochester, on hearing the name, set his teeth; near to him as I was, I felt the spasmodic movement of fury or despair run through his frame. The second stranger, who had hitherto lingered in the background, now drew near; it was Mason himself. Mr. Rochester turned and glared at him; his face flushed, and he stirred, lifted his strong arm—he could have dashed Mason on the church floor—but Mason shrank away, and cried faintly, "Good God!" Mr. Rochester's passion died as if a blight had shriveled it; he only asked, "What have *you* to say?"

An inaudible reply escaped Mason's white lips.

"The devil is in it if you cannot answer distinctly. I again demand, what have *you* to say?"

"Sir—sir—" interrupted the clergyman, "do not forget you are in a sacred place." Then addressing Mason, he inquired, "Are you aware, sir, whether or not this gentleman's wife is still living?"

"She is now living at Thornfield Hall," said Mason, in more articulate tones. "I saw her there last April. I am her brother."

"At Thornfield Hall!" ejaculated the clergyman. "Impossible! I am an old resident in this neighborhood, sir, and I never heard of a Mrs. Rochester at Thornfield Hall."

I saw a grim smile contort Mr. Rochester's lip, and he muttered, "No—by God! I took care that none should hear of it." He mused—then he formed his resolve, and announced it: "Enough. Wood, close your book, and take off your surplice; John Green [to the clerk], leave the church; there will be no wedding today." The man obeyed.

Mr. Rochester continued, hardily and recklessly, "Bigamy is an ugly word! I meant, however, to be a bigamist; but fate has outmaneuvered me, or Providence has checked me. Gentlemen, what this lawyer and his client say is true: I have been married, and the woman to whom I was married lives! You say you never heard of a Mrs. Rochester at the house up yonder, Wood; but I daresay you have many a time inclined your ear to gossip about the mysterious lunatic kept there under watch and ward. I now inform you that she is my wife, Bertha Mason by name. She is mad, and she came of a mad family. Her mother, the Creole, was both a madwoman and a drunkard—as I found out after I had wed the daughter. Bertha, like a dutiful child, copied her parent in both points. Oh, my experience has been heavenly, if you only knew it! But I owe you no further explanation. Briggs, Wood, Mason, I invite you all to come up to the house and visit Mrs. Poole's patient, and *my wife!* You shall see what sort of a being I was cheated into espousing, and judge whether or not I had a right to break the compact, and seek sympathy with something at least human. This girl," he continued, looking at me, "knew no more than you, Wood, of the disgusting secret; she thought all was fair and legal. Come all of you, follow!"

Still holding me fast, he left the church; the three gentlemen came after. At the front door of the hall we found the carriage.

"Take it back to the coach house, John," said Mr. Rochester, coolly; "it will not be wanted today."

At our entrance, Mrs. Fairfax, Adèle, Sophie, Leah advanced to meet and greet us.

"To the right about—every soul!" cried the master. "Away with your congratulations! Who wants them? Not I! They are fifteen years too late!"

He ascended the stairs, still holding my hand, the gentlemen following. We proceeded to the third story; the low, black door, opened by Mr. Rochester's key, admitted us to the tapestried room. "You know this place, Mason," said our guide; "she stabbed you here."

He lifted the hangings from the wall, uncovering the second door; this, too, he opened. In a room without a window, there burned a fire, guarded by a high and strong fender. Grace Poole bent over the fire, cooking something in a saucepan. In the deep shade, at the further end of the room, a figure moved backwards and forwards. What it was, whether beast or human being, one could not, at first sight, tell: it groveled on all fours; it growled like some strange wild animal; but it was covered with clothing, and a quantity of wild, dark hair hid its head and face.

"Good morrow, Mrs. Poole!" said Mr. Rochester. "How is your charge today?"

"We're tolerable, sir, I thank you," replied Grace, lifting the boiling mess carefully onto the hob; "rather snappish, but not 'rageous."

A fierce cry seemed to give the lie to her favorable report: the clothed hyena rose up, and stood tall on its feet.

"Ah, sir, she sees you!" exclaimed Grace; "you'd better not stay."

"You must allow me a few moments, Grace."

"Take care then, sir! For God's sake, take care!"

The maniac bellowed; she gazed wildly at her visitors. I recognized well that purple face, those bloated features.

"She has no knife, now, I suppose?" said Mr. Rochester. "I'm on my guard."

"One never knows what she has, sir: she is so cunning."

"We had better leave her," whispered Mason.

"Go to the devil!" was his brother-in-law's recommendation.

"'Ware!" cried Grace. The three gentlemen retreated simultaneously. Mr. Rochester flung me behind him; the lunatic sprang and grappled his throat viciously, and laid her teeth to his cheek; they struggled. She was a big woman, in stature almost equaling her husband; she showed virile force in the contest—more than once she almost throttled him, athletic as he was. He could have settled her with a well-planted blow, but he would not strike; he would only wrestle. At last he mastered her arms; Grace Poole gave him a cord, and he pinioned them behind her; with more rope he bound her to a chair. Mr. Rochester then turned to the spectators; he looked at them with a smile both acrid and desolate.

"That is *my wife*," said he. "Such is the sole conjugal embrace I am ever to know. And *this* is what I wished to have," laying his hand on my shoulder; "this young girl, who stands so grave and quiet at the mouth of hell. Wood and Briggs, look at the difference; then judge me, priest of the gospel and man of the law, and remember that with what judgment ye judge ye shall be judged. Off with you now. I must shut up my prize."

We all withdrew. Mr. Rochester stayed a moment behind us, to give some further order to Grace Poole. The solicitor addressed me as he descended the stair.

"You, madam," said he, "are cleared from all blame; your uncle will be glad to hear it—if, indeed, he should be still living—when Mr. Mason returns to Madeira."

"My uncle! Do you know him?"

"Mr. Mason does. When your uncle received your letter in-

timating the contemplated union between yourself and Mr.
Rochester, Mr. Mason, who was staying at Madeira to recruit his
health, on his way back to Jamaica, happened to be with him. Mr.
Eyre mentioned the intelligence, for he knew that my client here
was acquainted with a gentleman of the name of Rochester. Mr.
Mason, astonished and distressed as you may suppose, revealed the
real state of matters. Your uncle, I am sorry to say, is now on a
sickbed, from which it is unlikely he will ever rise. He could not
then hasten to England himself to extricate you from the snare
into which you had fallen, but he implored Mr. Mason to lose no
time in taking steps to prevent the false marriage. Were I not
morally certain that your uncle will be dead ere you reach Madeira,
I would advise you to accompany Mr. Mason back; but as it is, I
think you had better remain in England till you can hear further,
either from or of Mr. Eyre. Have we anything else to stay for?"
he inquired of Mr. Mason.

"No, no—let us be gone," was the anxious reply; and without
waiting to take leave of Mr. Rochester, they made their exit at
the hall door. The clergyman, too, departed.

The house cleared, I shut myself in my own room, fastened the
bolt that none might intrude, and proceeded—not to weep, not to
mourn, I was yet too calm for that, but—mechanically to take
off the wedding dress, and replace it by the stuff gown I had worn
yesterday. I felt weak and tired. And now I thought. Till now I had
only heard, seen, moved—watched event rush on event; but *now,
I thought*.

The morning had been a quiet morning enough—all except the
brief scene with the lunatic; the transaction in the church had not
been noisy: only a few words had been spoken. I was in my own
room now as usual—just myself, without obvious change; nothing
had smitten me, or scathed me, or maimed me. And yet where was
the Jane Eyre of yesterday? Where was her life? Where were her
prospects?

Jane Eyre, who had been an ardent, expectant woman—almost
a bride—was a cold, solitary girl again; her life was pale, her prospects were desolate. A Christmas frost had come at midsummer;

a white December storm had whirled over June; ice glazed the ripe apples, drifts crushed the blowing roses. I looked on my cherished wishes, yesterday so blooming and glowing; they lay stark, chill, livid corpses that could never revive. I looked at my love, that feeling which was my master's—which he had created; it shivered in my heart like a suffering child in a cold cradle; sickness and anguish had seized it; it could not seek Mr. Rochester's arms—it could not derive warmth from his breast. Oh, never more could it turn to him, for faith was blighted—confidence destroyed! Mr. Rochester was not to me what he had been, for he was not what I had thought him; I would not ascribe vice to him; I would not say he had betrayed me, but the attribute of stainless truth was gone from his idea; and from his presence I must go: that I perceived well. When—how—whither, I could not yet discern; but he himself, I doubted not, would hurry me from Thornfield. Real affection, it seemed, he could not have for me; it had been only fitful passion that was balked; he would want me no more. I should fear even to cross his path now; my view must be hateful to him. Oh, how blind had been my eyes! How weak my conduct!

My eyes were closed; eddying darkness seemed to swim round me, and reflection came in as black and confused a flow. I lay faint, longing to be dead. One idea only still throbbed lifelike within me—a remembrance of God. It begot an unuttered prayer:

"Be not far from me, for trouble is near: there is none to help."

It was near, and as I had lifted no petition to Heaven to avert it—as I had neither joined my hands, nor bent my knees, nor moved my lips—it came: the torrent poured over me. The whole consciousness of my life lorn, my love lost, my hope quenched, swayed full and mighty above me in one sullen mass. That bitter hour cannot be described. In truth, "the waters came into my soul; I sank in deep mire: I felt no standing; I came into deep waters; the floods overflowed me."

SOMETIME IN THE AFTERNOON I raised my head, and looking round and seeing the western sun gilding the sign of its decline on the wall, I asked: "What am I to do?"

But the answer my mind gave—"Leave Thornfield at once"—was so prompt, so dread, that I stopped my ears: I could not bear such words now. "That I am not Edward Rochester's bride is the least part of my woe," I alleged; "but that I must leave him instantly, entirely, is intolerable. I cannot do it."

I rose up suddenly, my head swimming. I perceived that I was sickening from excitement and inanition; neither meat nor drink had passed my lips that day, for I had taken no breakfast. And, with a strange pang, I now reflected that, long as I had been shut up here, no message had been sent to ask how I was or to invite me to come down; not even little Adèle had tapped at the door; not even Mrs. Fairfax had sought me.

As I undrew the bolt and went out I stumbled over an obstacle; my head was still dizzy, my limbs were feeble. I could not soon recover myself. I fell, but not onto the ground: an outstretched arm caught me; I looked up—I was supported by Mr. Rochester, who sat in a chair across my chamber threshold.

"You have come out at last," he said. "I have been waiting for you long, and listening, yet not one movement have I heard, nor one sob; five minutes more of that deathlike hush, and I should have forced the lock. So you shut yourself up and grieve alone! I expected a scene of some kind; I was prepared for the hot rain of tears, only I wanted them to be shed on my breast. Now a senseless floor has received them, or your drenched handkerchief. But I err; you have not wept at all! I see a white cheek and a faded eye, but no trace of tears. I suppose, then, your heart has been weeping blood?

"Jane, I never meant to wound you thus. If the man who had but one little ewe lamb that was dear to him as a daughter had by some mistake slaughtered it, he would not have rued his bloody blunder more than I now rue mine. Will you ever forgive me?"

Reader, I forgave him at the moment, and on the spot. There was such deep remorse in his eye, such unchanged love in his whole look and mien—I forgave him all; yet not outwardly, only at my heart's core.

"You know I am a scoundrel, Jane?" ere long he inquired wistfully—wondering, I suppose, at my continued silence and tameness: the result rather of weakness than of will.

"Yes, sir."

"Then tell me so roundly and sharply—don't spare me."

"I cannot; I am tired and sick. I want some water." He heaved a sort of shuddering sigh, and taking me in his arms, carried me downstairs. At first I did not know to what room he had borne me; all was cloudy to my glazed sight. Presently I felt the reviving warmth of a fire; I had become icy cold in my chamber. He put wine to my lips; I tasted it and revived; then I ate something he offered me, and was soon myself. I was in the library—sitting in his chair—he was quite near. If I could go out of life now, without too sharp a pang, it would be well for me, I thought; then I should not have to make the effort of cracking my heartstrings in rending them from among Mr. Rochester's. I did not want to leave him— I could not leave him.

"How are you now, Jane?"

"Much better, sir; I shall be well soon."

"Taste the wine again, Jane."

I obeyed him. He looked at me attentively, then turned away, with an inarticulate exclamation, full of passionate emotion of some kind; he walked fast through the room and came back; he stooped toward me as if to kiss me, but I remembered caresses were now forbidden. I turned my face away, and put his aside.

"What! How is this?" he exclaimed hastily. "Oh, I know! You won't kiss the husband of Bertha Mason? You consider my arms filled?"

"At any rate, there is neither room nor claim for me, sir."

"Why, Jane? I will spare you the trouble of much talking; I will answer for you—because I have a wife already, you would reply. I guess rightly?"

"Yes."

"If you think so, you must have a strange opinion of me; you must regard me as a profligate—a low rake who has been simulating love in order to draw you into a snare. What do you say to that? I see you can say nothing; you are thinking how *to act*—

talking, you consider, is of no use. I know you—I am on my guard."

"Sir, I do not wish to act against you," I said, and my unsteady voice warned me to curtail my sentence.

"Not in *your* sense of the word but in *mine*, you are scheming to destroy me. You have as good as said that I am a married man—as a married man you will shun me; just now you have refused to kiss me. You intend to make yourself a stranger to me; if ever a friendly feeling inclines you again to me, you will say, 'That man nearly made me his mistress; I must be ice and rock to him.'"

I steadied my voice to reply, "All is changed about me, sir; I must change too; and to avoid fluctuations of feeling, and continual combats with recollections and associations, there is only one way—Adèle must have a new governess, sir."

"Oh, Adèle will go to school—I have settled that already; nor do I mean to torment you with the hideous associations and recollections of Thornfield Hall. You shall not stay here, nor will I. I was wrong ever to bring you to this place, knowing as I did how it was haunted. I charged them to conceal from you, before I ever saw you, all knowledge of the curse of the place; merely because I feared Adèle never would have a governess to stay if she knew with what inmate she was housed, and my plans would not permit me to remove the maniac elsewhere—though I possess an old house, Ferndean Manor, even more retired than this, where I could have lodged her, had not a scruple about the unhealthiness of the situation, in the heart of a wood, made my conscience recoil from the arrangement.

"But I'll shut up Thornfield Hall; I'll nail up the front door; I'll give Mrs. Poole two hundred a year to live here with *my wife*, as you term that fearful hag. Grace will do much for money, and she shall have her son, the keeper at Grimsby Retreat, to bear her company and be at hand to give her aid, in the paroxysms, when *my wife* is prompted to stab people, to bite their flesh—"

"Sir," I interrupted him, "you are inexorable for that unfortunate lady; you speak of her with hate. But she cannot help being mad."

"Jane, my little darling, you don't know what you are talking about; it is not because she is mad I hate her. If you were mad, do you think I should hate you?"

"I do indeed, sir."

"Then you are mistaken. Every atom of your flesh is as dear to me as my own: in pain, sickness or madness it would still be dear. But why follow that train of ideas? I was talking of removing you from Thornfield, and tomorrow you shall go. I only ask you to endure one more night under this roof, Jane, and then, farewell to its miseries and forever! I have a place to repair to, which will be a secure sanctuary from hateful reminiscences."

"Take Adèle with you, sir," I interrupted; "she will be a companion for you."

"What do you mean, Jane? I told you I would send Adèle to school."

"You spoke of a retirement, sir; and retirement and solitude are dull—too dull for you."

"Solitude!" he repeated. "I see I must come to an explanation. *You* are to share my solitude. Do you understand?"

I shook my head: it required courage, excited as he was becoming, even to risk that sign of dissent. He had been walking fast about the room, and he stopped, as if suddenly rooted to one spot. He looked at me hard; I turned my eyes from him, fixed them on the fire, and tried to assume a quiet, collected aspect.

"Now for the hitch in Jane's character," he said at last. "The reel of silk has run smoothly enough so far; but I always knew there would come a knot. Here it is."

He recommenced his walk, but soon again stopped, and this time just before me.

"Jane, will you hear reason?" He stooped and approached his lips to my ear. "Because, if you won't, I'll try violence." His voice was hoarse, his look that of a man who is just about to burst an insufferable bond and plunge headlong into wild license. I had been struggling with tears for some time; I had taken great pains to repress them; now, however, I considered it well to let them flow; if the flood annoyed him, so much the better. So I gave way and cried heartily. Soon I heard him earnestly entreating me to be composed. I said I could not while he was in such a passion.

"But I am not angry, Jane; I only love you too well. Hush, now, and wipe your eyes."

His softened voice announced that he was subdued; so I, in my turn, became calm. Now he made an effort to rest his head on my shoulder, but I would not permit it.

"Jane! Jane!" he said, in an accent of bitter sadness. "You don't love me, then? It was only my station and the rank of my wife that you valued?"

These words cut me, and I could not control the wish to drop balm where I had wounded. "I *do* love you," I said, "more than ever; but I must not indulge the feeling, and this is the last time I must express it."

"The last time, Jane! What! Do you think you can see me daily, and yet, if you still love me, be always cold and distant?"

"No, sir; that I am certain I could not; and therefore I see there is but one way: I must leave you, Mr. Rochester."

"For how long, Jane? For a few minutes, while you smooth your hair—and bathe your face?"

"I must leave Thornfield. I must part with you. I must begin a new existence amongst strange faces and strange scenes."

"Of course, I told you you should. I pass over the madness about parting from me. You mean you must become a part of me. As to the new existence, it is all right; you shall yet be my wife; I am not married. You shall be Mrs. Rochester—both virtually and nominally. I shall keep only to you so long as you and I live! You shall go to a place I have in the south of France, a white-washed villa; there you shall live a happy, and guarded and most innocent life. Never fear that I wish to lure you into error—to make you my mistress. Why do you shake your head? Jane, you must be reasonable, or in truth I shall again become frantic."

His eye blazed; still I dared to speak. "Sir, your wife is living: if I lived with you as you desire, I should then be your mistress; to say otherwise is false."

He drew a long breath. "I am a fool!" he said at last. "I keep telling her I am not married, and do not explain to her why. I forget she knows nothing of the circumstances attending my infernal union with that woman. Oh, I am certain Jane will agree with me in opinion when she knows all that I know! Janet—can you listen to me?"

"Yes, sir; for hours if you will."

"I ask only minutes. Jane, did you ever hear, or know that I had once a brother older than I?"

"I remember Mrs. Fairfax told me so once."

"And did you ever hear that my father was an avaricious, grasping man?"

"I think not."

"Well, Jane, he was; and being so, it was his resolution to keep the property together; he could not bear the idea of dividing his estate and leaving me a fair portion; all, he resolved, should go to my brother, Rowland. Yet as little could he endure that a son of his should be a poor man: I must be provided for by a wealthy marriage. Mr. Mason, a rich West India planter, was his old acquaintance. Mr. Mason, he found, had a son and daughter; and he learned from him that he could and would give the latter a fortune of thirty thousand pounds. That sufficed. When I left college, I was sent out to Jamaica, to espouse a bride already courted for me. My father told me Bertha Mason was the boast of Spanish Town for her beauty, and this was no lie. I found her a fine woman, tall, dark, majestic. Her family wished to secure me because I was of a good race; and so did she. They showed her to me in parties, splendidly dressed. I seldom saw her alone, and had very little private conversation with her. All the men in her circle seemed to admire her and envy me. I was dazzled, stimulated; and being ignorant and inexperienced, I thought I loved her. Her relations encouraged me; a marriage was achieved almost before I knew where I was. Oh, I have no respect for myself when I think of that act! I never loved, I never esteemed, I did not even know her.

"My bride's mother I had never seen: I understood she was dead. The honeymoon over, I learned my mistake; she was shut up in a lunatic asylum. There was a younger brother, too, a complete dumb idiot. The elder one, whom you have seen (and whom

I cannot hate, because he has some grains of affection in his feeble mind), will probably be in the same state one day. My father and my brother Rowland knew all this; but they thought only of the thirty thousand pounds, and joined in the plot against me.

"These were vile discoveries; but, except for the treachery of concealment, I should have made them no subject of reproach to my wife: even when I found her nature wholly alien to mine, her cast of mind low and narrow—when I found that I could not pass a single hour of the day with her in comfort. When I perceived that I should never have a quiet or settled household, because no servant would bear the continued outbreaks of her violent temper, even then I restrained myself.

"Jane, I will not trouble you with abominable details. I lived with that woman four years, and before that time she had tried me indeed. Her character developed with frightful rapidity; her vices sprang up fast and rank; they were so strong, only cruelty could check them, and I would not use cruelty.

"My brother in the interval was dead; my father too. I was rich enough now—yet poor; a nature the most depraved I ever saw was associated with mine, and called by the law a part of me. And I could not rid myself of it by any legal proceedings, for the doctors now discovered that *my wife* was mad—her excesses had prematurely developed the germs of insanity. Jane, you don't like my narrative; you look almost sick—shall I defer the rest to another day?"

"No, sir, finish it now. I pity you—I do earnestly pity you. Proceed. What did you do when you found she was mad?"

"Jane, I approached the verge of despair: a remnant of self-respect was all that intervened between me and the gulf. One night I had been awakened by her yells—since the medical men had pronounced her mad, she had of course been shut up—it was a fiery West Indian night, one of the description that frequently precedes the hurricanes of those climates. Being unable to sleep in bed, I got up and opened the window. I was physically influenced by the atmosphere, and my ears were filled with the curses the maniac still shrieked out.

"'This life,' said I at last, 'is hell! I have a right to deliver myself from it if I can.' I said this whilst I knelt down and unlocked a trunk which contained a loaded pistol. I meant to shoot myself. I only entertained the intention for a moment; for, not being insane, I passed in a second the crisis of despair which had originated the wish of self-destruction.

"A wind fresh from Europe blew over the ocean and rushed through the casement; the storm which had been approaching broke, streamed, thundered, blazed, and the air grew pure. I then framed a resolution. While I walked under the dripping orange trees of my wet garden, I saw Hope revive. From a flowery arch at the bottom of my garden I gazed over the blue sea; the old world was beyond; clear prospects opened thus:

"'Go,' said Hope, 'and live again in Europe; there it is not known what a filthy burden is bound to you. Take the maniac to England; confine her with due attendance at Thornfield; then travel yourself to what clime you will, and form what new tie you like. That woman who has so blighted your youth is not your wife. See that she is cared for as her condition demands, and you have done all that God and Humanity require of you. Place her in safety and comfort; shelter her degradation with secrecy, and leave her.'

"I acted precisely on this suggestion. My father and brother had not made my marriage known to their acquaintance; because, in the very first letter I wrote to apprise them of the union, and seeing a hideous future opening to me, I added an urgent charge to keep it secret; and very soon the infamous conduct of the wife my father had selected for me was such as to make him blush to own her as his daughter-in-law.

"To England, then, I conveyed her. Glad was I when I at last got her to Thornfield, and saw her safely lodged in that third-story room. I had some trouble in finding an attendant for her, as it was necessary to select one on whose fidelity dependence could be placed; at last I hired Grace Poole from the Grimsby Retreat. She and the surgeon, Carter, who dressed Mason's wounds that night, are the only two I have ever admitted to my confidence, though Mrs. Fairfax may indeed have suspected something. Grace has, on the whole, proved a good keeper; though, owing partly to a fault of her own, of which it appears nothing can cure her, her vigilance has been more than once lulled. The lunatic is both cunning and malignant; she has never failed to take advantage of her guardian's lapses; once to secrete the knife with which she stabbed her brother, and twice to possess herself of the key of her cell. On the first of these occasions, she attempted to burn me in my bed; on the second she paid that ghastly visit to you. I thank Providence, who watched over you, that she then spent her fury on your wedding apparel."

"And what, sir," I asked, while he paused, "did you do when you had settled her here?"

"What did I do, Jane? I sought the Continent, and went through all its lands. My fixed desire was to seek and find a good and intelligent woman whom I could love."

"But you could not marry, sir."

"I was convinced that I could and ought. It was not my original intention to deceive, as I have deceived you. I meant to make my proposals openly; I never doubted some woman might be found willing and able to understand my case and accept me."

"Well, sir? Did you find anyone you liked? What did she say?"

"I can tell you whether I found anyone I liked; but what she said is yet to be recorded in the book of Fate. For ten long years I roved about, living first in one capital, then another. Provided with plenty of money, I could choose my own society. I sought my ideal of a woman amongst English ladies, French countesses, Italian signoras, and German gräfinnen. I could not find her. Disappointment made me reckless. I tried dissipation; and I could not live alone, so I tried the companionship of mistresses. But, Jane, I see by your face you are not forming a very favorable opinion of me just now. You think me a loose-principled rake, don't you?"

"I don't like you so well as I have done sometimes, indeed, sir. Did it not seem to you wrong to live in that way?"

"I did not like it; I should never like to return to it. But, Jane, let me come to the point. Last January, in a harsh, bitter frame of mind, recalled by business, I came back to England. On a frosty winter afternoon I rode in sight of Thornfield Hall. Abhorred spot! I expected no peace, no pleasure there. On a stile in Hay Lane I saw a quiet little figure sitting by itself. I passed it negligently: I had no presentiment of what it would be to me— not even when, on the occasion of Mesrour's accident, it gravely offered me help. Childish and slender creature! It seemed as if a linnet had hopped to my foot and proposed to bear me on its tiny wing. I was surly; but the thing would not go: it stood by me with strange perseverance, and looked and spoke with a sort of authority. I must be aided, and by that hand, and aided I was.

"When once I had pressed the frail shoulder, something new stole into my frame. It was well I had learnt that this elf belonged to my house—or I could not have let it pass away from under my hand. I heard you come home that night, Jane, though probably you were not aware that I watched for you. The next day I observed you—myself unseen—for half an hour, while you played with Adèle in the gallery.

"Impatiently I waited for evening, when I might summon you to my presence. An unusual—to me—a perfectly new character, I suspected was yours; I desired to search it deeper, and know it better. You entered the room with a look and air at once shy and independent. I made you talk. I was at once content and stimulated with what I saw; yet, for a long time, I treated you distantly, and sought your company rarely; I was fearful that if I handled the flower too freely its bloom would fade. At this time I used to enjoy a chance meeting with you, Jane: there was a curious hesitation in your manner; you glanced at me with a hovering doubt; you did not know whether I was going to play the master and be stern, or the friend and be benignant. I was now too fond of you often to simulate the first whim; and, when I stretched my hand out cordially, such bloom and light and bliss rose to your young, wistful features, I had much ado often to avoid straining you then and there to my heart."

"Don't talk anymore of those days, sir," I interrupted, dashing away some tears from my eyes; his language was torture to me, for I knew what I must do—and do soon—and all these reminiscences and revelations only made my work more difficult.

"You see now how the case stands, do you not?" he continued. "After a youth and manhood passed half in unutterable misery and half in dreary solitude, I have for the first time found what I can truly love—I have found *you*. You are my better self—my good angel. Because I felt and knew this, I resolved to marry you. I was wrong to attempt to deceive you; but I feared a stubbornness that exists in your character; I feared early-instilled prejudice. This was cowardly: I should have appealed to your nobleness and magnanimity at first, as I do now—opened to you plainly my life of agony—and described to you my hunger and thirst after a higher and worthier existence. Then I should have asked you to accept my pledge of fidelity, and to give me yours. Jane—give it me now."

A pause.

"Why are you silent, Jane?"

I was experiencing an ordeal: a hand of fiery iron grasped my vitals. Terrible moment: full of struggle, blackness, burning! Not a human being that ever lived could wish to be loved better than I was loved; and him who thus loved me I absolutely worshiped; and I must renounce love and idol. One drear word comprised my intolerable duty—Depart!

"Jane, you understand what I want of you? Just this promise— 'I will be yours, Mr. Rochester.'"

"Mr. Rochester, I will *not* be yours."

Another long silence.

"Jane!" recommenced he. "Jane, do you mean to go one way in the world, and to let me go another?"

"I do."

"Oh, Jane, this is bitter! This—this is wicked. It would not be wicked to love me."

"It would to obey you."

A wild look raised his brows—crossed his features; he rose. I laid my hand on a chair for support: I shook, I feared—but I resolved.

"One instant, Jane. Give one glance to my horrible life when you are gone. All happiness will be torn away with you. What shall I do, Jane? Where turn for a companion, and for some hope?"

"Do as I do: trust in God and yourself. Believe in Heaven. Hope to meet again there."

"Then you condemn me to live wretched, and to die accursed?"

"I advise you to live sinless, and I wish you to die tranquil. We were born to strive and endure—you as well as I. Do so. We must keep the law given by God; laws and principles are not for the times when there is no temptation; they are for such moments as this, when body and soul rise in mutiny against their rigor. Foregone determinations are all I have at this hour to stand by; there I plant my foot."

I did. Mr. Rochester saw I had done so. His fury was wrought to the highest. He crossed the floor, grasped my waist and seemed to devour me with his flaming glance. Physically, I felt at the moment powerless as stubble exposed to a furnace; mentally, I still possessed my soul. The soul, fortunately, has an interpreter in the eye. My eye rose to his; and while I looked in his fierce face, I gave an involuntary sigh: his grip was painful, and my overtasked strength almost exhausted.

"Never," said he, as he ground his teeth, "never was anything at once so frail and so indomitable. A mere reed she feels!" And he shook me with the force of his hold. "I could bend her with my finger and thumb, and what good would it do? Consider that eye: consider the resolute, wild, free thing looking out of it, defying me. Whatever I do with its cage, I cannot get at it, the savage, beautiful creature! And it is you, spirit, that I want. Oh, come, Jane, come!"

As he said this, he released me from his clutch, and only looked at me. The look was far worse to resist than the frantic strain: I must elude his sorrow. I retired to the door.

"You are going, Jane?"

"I am going, sir."

"You are leaving me? You will not be my comforter, my rescuer? My love, my woe, my prayer, are nothing to you?"

What unutterable pathos was in his voice! How hard it was to reiterate firmly, "I am going."

"Jane!"

"Mr. Rochester!"

"Withdraw, then—I consent—but remember, you leave me here in anguish. Go up to your own room; think over all I have said, Jane—think of me."

He turned away; he threw himself on his face on the sofa. "Oh, Jane! My hope—my love—my life!" broke in anguish from his lips. Then came a deep, strong sob.

I had already gained the door; but, reader, I walked back. I knelt down by him; I turned his face from the cushion to me; I kissed his cheek; I smoothed his hair with my hand. "God bless you, my dear master!" I said. "God keep you from harm and wrong—direct you, solace you—reward you well for your past kindness to me."

"Little Jane's love would have been my best reward," he answered; "without it, my heart is broken. But Jane will give me her love, yes—nobly, generously."

Up the blood rushed to his face; erect he sprang; he held his arms out; but I evaded the embrace, and at once quitted the room.

"Farewell!" was the cry of my heart as I left him. Despair added, "Farewell, forever!"

THAT NIGHT I NEVER thought to sleep; but a slumber fell on me as soon as I lay down in bed. When I awoke it was yet night, but July nights are short. Thought I, It cannot be too early to commence the task I have to fulfill. I rose; I was dressed, for I had taken off nothing but my shoes. I knew where to find in my drawers some linen, a locket, a ring. These articles I made up into a parcel; my purse, containing twenty shillings (it was all I had), I put in my pocket; I tied on my straw bonnet, pinned my shawl, took the parcel and stole from my room.

"Farewell, kind Mrs. Fairfax!" I whispered, as I glided past her door. "Farewell, my darling Adèle!" I said as I glanced towards the nursery.

I would have got past Mr. Rochester's chamber without a pause; but my heart momentarily stopping its beat at that threshold, my foot was forced to stop also. No sleep was there: the inmate was walking restlessly from wall to wall. There was a heaven—a temporary heaven—in this room for me, if I chose: I had but to go in and to say, "Mr. Rochester, I love you and will live with you—" and a fount of rapture would spring to my lips.

My hand moved towards the lock; I caught it back, and glided on. Drearily I wound my way downstairs. In the kitchen I drank some water, I ate some bread, for perhaps I should have to walk

far. All this I did without one sound. I opened the kitchen door, passed out, shut it softly. Dim dawn glimmered in the yard. The great gates were closed and locked; but a wicket in one of them was only latched. Through that I departed; it, too, I shut, and now I was out of Thornfield.

A mile off, beyond the fields, lay a road which stretched in the contrary direction to Millcote, a road I had never traveled; thither I bent my steps. I skirted fields and hedges till after sunrise. I believe it was a lovely summer morning, but I looked neither to rising sun, nor smiling sky, nor wakening nature. He who is taken out to pass through a fair scene to the scaffold thinks not of the flowers that smile on his road; but of the block and axe edge; of the disseverment of bone and vein; of the grave gaping at the end. When I got to the road I rested under the hedge; and while I sat, I saw a coach come on. I stood up and lifted my hand; it stopped. It was going to a place a long way off, and where I was sure Mr. Rochester had no connections. I asked for what sum the driver would take me there; he said thirty shillings; I answered I had but twenty; well, he would try to make it do. I entered—the vehicle was empty—I was shut in, and it rolled on its way.

Gentle reader, may you never feel what I then felt! May your eyes never shed such stormy, scalding, heart-wrung tears as poured from mine. May you never appeal to Heaven in prayers so hopeless and so agonized as that hour left my lips; for never may you, like me, dread to be the instrument of evil to what you wholly love.

CHAPTER XIV

TWO DAYS ARE PASSED. It is a summer evening; the coachman has set me down at a place called Whitcross; he could take me no farther for the sum I had given, and I had not another shilling in the world. The coach is a mile off by this time; I am alone. At this moment I discover that I forgot to take my parcel out of the coach; and now I am absolutely destitute.

Whitcross is not even a hamlet; it is but a stone pillar set up where four roads meet. Four arms spring from its summit; the nearest town to which these point is distant ten miles. From the well-known names of these towns I learn in what county I have lighted—a north-midland shire. There are great moors on each hand of me, with mountains far beyond; on the moors the heather grows deep and wild. The population here must be thin, and I see no passengers on these roads; yet a chance traveler might pass by, and I wish no eye to see me now: strangers would wonder what I am doing, lingering here, evidently objectless and lost.

I struck straight into the heath; I held on to a hollow I saw deeply furrowing the brown moorside; I turned with its turnings, and, finding a moss-blackened granite crag in a hidden angle, I sat down under it. Some time passed before I felt tranquil. Calmed, however, by the deep silence that reigned as evening declined, I took confidence. I had one morsel of bread yet, the remnant of a roll I had bought, with a last stray penny, in a town we passed through at noon; I ate it, and my hunger was, if not satisfied, appeased. I touched the heath: it was dry, and yet warm with the heat of the summer day. I looked at the sky; it was pure: a kindly star twinkled just above the chasm ridge. The dew fell but with propitious softness; no breeze whispered. Beside the crag, the heath was very deep, rising high on each side of me. I spread my shawl over me for a coverlet. Thus lodged, I was not cold, and my rest might have been blissful enough, only a sad heart broke it, trembling for Mr. Rochester and his doom, demanding him with ceaseless longing.

Worn out with this torture of thought, I rose to my knees. Night was come, and her planets were risen: a safe, still night. We know that God is everywhere; but certainly we feel His presence most when His works are on the grandest scale spread before us. I had risen to my knees to pray for Mr. Rochester. Looking up, I, with tear-dimmed eyes, saw the mighty Milky Way. Remembering what it was—what countless systems swept space like a soft trace of light—I felt the might and strength of God.

At last I slept. Next day, when the long morning shadows were curtailed, and the sun filled earth and sky, I got up, and I looked round me. What a still, hot, perfect day! What a golden desert this spreading moor! I wished I could live in it and on it. I saw a lizard run over the crag; I saw a bee busy among the bilberries. I fain would have become bee or lizard. But I had a human being's wants; I must not linger where there was nothing to supply them. I rose and set out.

Whitcross regained, I followed a road which led from the sun, now fervent and high. I walked a long time, and at last, when I thought I must yield to the fatigue that almost overpowered me, there, amongst the romantic hills, I saw a hamlet and a spire. Human life and human labor were near. I must struggle on. At about two o'clock p.m., I entered the village. At the bottom of its one street, there was a little shop with some cakes of bread in the window. I coveted a cake of bread. With that refreshment I could perhaps regain a degree of energy. Had I nothing about me I could offer in exchange for one of these rolls? I had a small silk handkerchief tied round my throat; I had my gloves. I did not know whether either of these articles would be accepted, but I must try.

I entered the shop; a woman was there. Seeing a respectably dressed person, she came forward with civility. How could she serve me? I was seized with shame: I dared not offer her the half-worn gloves, the creased handkerchief. I only begged permission to sit down a moment, as I was tired. Disappointed in the expectation of a customer, she coolly acceded to my request. Soon I asked her if there were any dressmaker or plain-work woman in the village.

"Yes, two or three. Quite as many as there is employment for."

I reflected. I must do something. What?

"Do you know of any place in the neighborhood where a servant is wanted?"

"Nay; I couldn't say."

"What is the chief trade in this place?"

"Some are farm laborers; a good deal work at Mr. Oliver's needle factory, and at the foundry."

"Does Mr. Oliver employ women?"

"Nay; it is men's work."

She seemed to be tired of my questions; and, indeed, what claim had I to importune her? I took leave.

I walked along the street, looking at all the houses; but I could discover no pretext to enter any. Much exhausted, and suffering greatly now for want of food, I turned aside into a lane and sat down under a hedge. Ere many minutes had elapsed, I was again on my feet, however, and again searching something—a resource, or at least an informant.

A pretty little house stood at the top of the lane; I stopped at it and knocked at its white door. A mild-looking, cleanly attired young woman opened the door. In such a voice as might be expected from a hopeless heart and fainting frame I asked if a servant was wanted here.

"No," said she; "we do not keep a servant."

"Can you tell me where I could get employment of any kind?"

But it was not her business to seek a place for me; besides, in her eyes, how doubtful must have appeared my character and position. She shook her head, she was sorry she could give me no information, and the white door closed, quite gently and civilly.

I tried at other houses, but with the same success. Meantime, the afternoon advanced, while I thus wandered about like a lost and starving dog. A little before dark I passed a farmhouse, at the open door of which the farmer was sitting, eating his supper of bread and cheese. I stopped, and said, "Will you give me a piece of bread? I am very hungry." He cast on me a glance of surprise; but without answering, he cut a thick slice from his loaf, and gave it to me. I imagine he thought I was an eccentric sort of lady, who had taken a fancy to his brown loaf. As soon as I was out of sight of his house, I sat down and ate it.

I could not hope to get a lodging under a roof, and eventually I sought it in a nearby wood. But my night was wretched, my rest broken; the ground was damp, the air cold; toward morning it rained.

Do not ask me, reader, to give a minute account of the following day; as before, I sought work; as before, I was repulsed; as before, I starved; but once did food pass my lips. At the door of a cottage I saw a little girl about to throw a mess of cold porridge into a pig trough. "Will you give me that?" I asked.

She stared at me. "Mother!" she exclaimed. "There is a woman wants me to give her the porridge."

"Well, lass," replied a voice within, "give it her if she's a beggar. T' pig doesn't want it."

The girl emptied the stiffened mold into my hand, and I devoured it ravenously.

As the wet twilight deepened, I stopped in a solitary bridle path, which I had been pursuing an hour or more. It was again night time, I must again seek shelter. My glazed eye wandered over the dim and misty landscape. I saw I had strayed far from the village: it was quite out of sight; I had once more drawn near the moorland. My eye roved over the sullen swell, and along the moor edge, vanishing amidst the wildest scenery; when at one dim point, far in among the marshes and the ridges, a light sprang up. That is an *ignis fatuus*, was my first thought; and I expected it would vanish. It burned on, however. It may be a candle in a house, I conjectured, but if so, I can never reach it. And were it within a yard of me, what would it avail? I should but knock at the door to have it shut in my face.

I sank down where I stood, and hid my face against the ground. The night wind swept over the hill and over me, and died moaning in the distance; the rain fell fast, wetting me to the skin. My yet living flesh shuddered, and I rose. The light was still there, shining dim, but constant, through the rain: I dragged my exhausted limbs towards it.

Having crossed a marsh, I saw a track over the moor. It led straight up to the light, which now beamed from a sort of knoll. I groped on. A white gate gleamed before me; as I entered it the silhouette of a low house rose to view, but the guiding light shone nowhere. In seeking the door, I turned an angle; there shot out the friendly gleam again from the panes of a small latticed window, made still smaller by the growth of ivy whose leaves clustered thick over the house wall.

When I put aside the spray of foliage shooting over the window, I could see all within: a room with a sanded floor, clean scoured; a dresser of walnut, with pewter plates ranged in rows, reflecting the redness of a glowing peat fire. The candle, whose ray had been my beacon, burned on a table; and by its light an elderly woman was knitting a stocking.

Near the hearth, amidst the rosy peace suffusing it, sat two young, graceful women—ladies in every point; both wore deep mourning, which somber garb singularly set off very fair necks and faces; a large old pointer dog rested its massive head on the knee of one girl—in the lap of the other was cushioned a black cat. Who were these girls? They could not be the daughters of the elderly person at the table, for she looked like a rustic, and they were all grace and cultivation. I cannot call them handsome—they were too pale and grave for the word as they each bent over a book. A stand between them supported a second candle and two great volumes, to which they frequently referred, like people consulting a dictionary to aid them in translation. This scene was so hushed that I could hear the cinders fall from the grate, the clock tick in its obscure corner; when, therefore, a voice broke the stillness, it was audible enough to me.

"Listen, Diana," said one of the absorbed students: "Franz and old Daniel are together in the night time, and Franz is telling a dream from which he has awakened in terror—listen!" And in a low voice she read something, of which not one word was intelligible to me.

"Is there ony country where they talk i' that way?" asked the old woman, looking up from her knitting.

"Yes, Hannah—Germany is a far larger country than England, and there they talk in no other way."

"Well, for sure case, I knawn't how they can understand t' one t' other. And what good does it do you to learn to speak that way?"

"We mean to teach it sometime, and then we shall get more money than we do now."

"Varry like: but give ower studying; ye've done enough for tonight."

"I think we have; at least I'm tired. Mary, are you?"

"Mortally. I wonder when St. John will come home."

"Surely he will not be long now: it is just ten"— looking at a little gold watch she drew from her girdle. "Hannah, will you have the goodness to look at the fire in the parlor?"

The woman rose; soon I heard her stir a fire in an inner room. The ladies also rose; they seemed about to withdraw to the parlor. Till this moment, I had been so intent on watching them I had half forgotten my own wretched position; now it recurred to me. More desolate than ever, it seemed from contrast. And how impossible did it appear to touch the inmates of this house with

concern on my behalf. As I groped for the door, and knocked at it hesitatingly, I felt that last idea to be a mere chimera. Hannah opened.

"What do you want?" she inquired, in a voice of surprise, as she surveyed me by the light of the candle she held.

"May I speak to your mistresses?" I said.

"You had better tell me what you have to say to them. What is your business here at this hour?"

"I want a night's shelter in an outhouse or anywhere, and a morsel of bread to eat."

Distrust appeared in Hannah's face. "I'll give you a penny," she said, after a pause; "but we can't take in a vagrant to lodge. Here is a penny; now go."

"A penny cannot feed me, and I have no strength to go farther. Don't shut the door, for God's sake!"

"I must; the rain is driving in."

"Tell the young ladies. Let me see them—I must die if I am turned away."

"Not you. I'm fear'd you have some ill plans agate, that bring you about folk's houses at this time o' night." Here the honest but inflexible servant clapped the door to and bolted it within.

This was the climax. A throe of true despair rent my heart. Worn out, indeed, I was; not another step could I stir. I sank on the wet doorstep; I wept in utter anguish.

"I can but die," I said aloud, "and I believe in God. Let me try to wait His will in silence."

"All men must die," said a voice close at hand; "but all are not condemned to meet a lingering and premature doom, such as yours would be if you perished here of want."

"Who or what speaks?" I asked, terrified at the unexpected sound. A form was near—what form, I could not distinguish. With a loud knock, the newcomer appealed to the door.

"Is it you, Mr. St. John?" cried Hannah.

"Yes—yes; open quickly."

"Well, how wet and cold you must be. Come in—your sisters are quite uneasy about you, and I believe there are bad folks about. There has been a beggarwoman—I declare she is not gone yet! Get up! For shame! Move off, I say!"

"Hush, Hannah! I have a word to say to the woman. You have done your duty in excluding, now let me do mine in admitting her. I was near, and listened to both you and her. Young woman, rise, and pass before me into the house."

With difficulty I obeyed him. Presently I stood within that bright kitchen, trembling, sickening. The two ladies, their brother, the old servant, were all gazing at me.

"St. John, who is it?" I heard one ask.

"I cannot tell. I found her at the door," was the reply.

"She does look white," said Hannah.

"As white as clay or death," was responded. "She will fall; let her sit."

And indeed my head swam. I dropped, but a chair received me. I still possessed my senses, though just now I could not speak.

"Perhaps a little water would restore her. Hannah, fetch some. But she is worn to nothing!"

"A mere specter!"

"Is she ill, or only famished?"

"Famished, I think. Hannah, is that milk? Give it me, and a piece of bread."

One sister—I later learned she was Diana—broke some bread, dipped it in milk, and put it to my lips. I saw there was sympathy in her face. In her simple words, too, the same balmlike emotion spoke: "Try to eat."

"Yes—try," gently repeated the other sister, Mary; and Mary's hand removed my sodden bonnet and lifted my head. I tasted what they offered me, feebly at first, eagerly soon.

"Try if she can speak now," said the brother. "Ask her her name."

I felt I could speak, and I answered, "My name is Jane Elliott." Anxious as ever to avoid discovery, I had resolved to assume an alias.

"And where do you live? Where are your friends?"

I was silent.

"Can we send for anyone you know?"

I shook my head.

Somehow, now that I had once crossed the threshold of this house, I felt no longer outcast, vagrant. I dared to put off the mendicant—to resume my natural manner; and when Mr. St. John demanded an account—which I was far too weak to render—I said after a pause:

"Sir, I can give you no details tonight."

"But what, then," said he, "do you expect me to do for you?"

I looked at his sisters. They had, I thought, remarkable countenances, instinct with goodness. I took sudden courage. "I can only trust you," I said. "Do for me as you like; but excuse me from much discourse—I feel a spasm when I speak." All three surveyed me silently.

"Hannah," said Mr. St. John, at last, "let her sit there at present, and ask her no questions. Mary and Diana, let us go into the parlor and talk the matter over."

They withdrew. Soon one of the ladies returned; I could not tell which. A kind of pleasant stupor was stealing over me. In an undertone she gave some directions to Hannah. Ere long, with the servant's aid, I contrived to mount a staircase; my dripping clothes were removed; a warm, dry bed received me. I thanked God—experienced amidst unutterable exhaustion a glow of grateful joy—and slept.

CHAPTER XV

THE RECOLLECTION OF ABOUT THREE DAYS and nights succeeding this is very dim in my mind. I observed when anyone entered or left my bedroom; I could understand what was said when the speaker stood near to me, but I could not answer. Hannah, the servant, was my most frequent visitor; I had a feeling that she wished me away. Diana and Mary appeared in the chamber once or twice a day. They would whisper sentences of this sort at my bedside: "It is very well we took her in."

"Yes; she would certainly have died had she been left out all night. I wonder what she has gone through?"

"Strange hardships, I imagine. But she is not an uneducated person, by her manner."

On the third day, I was better; on the fourth, I could speak, and move. Hannah had brought me some gruel and toast, about the dinner hour: I had eaten with relish. When she left me, I felt comparatively strong and revived, and I wished to rise. On a chair by the bedside were all my own things, now clean and dry. After a weary process, and resting every five minutes, I succeeded in dressing myself, and creeping down a stone staircase, I found my way presently to the kitchen. It was full of the fragrance of new bread; Hannah was baking. Latterly she had begun to relent a little towards me; and when she saw me come in tidy and well-dressed, she even smiled.

"What, you have got up?" she said. "You are better, then. You may sit you down in my chair on the hearthstone, if you will."

She pointed to the rocking chair; I took it. Turning to me, as she took some loaves from the oven, she asked, bluntly:

"Did you ever go a-begging afore you came here?"

I was indignant for a moment; but remembering that anger was out of the question, I answered quietly, "I am no beggar, any more than yourself or your young ladies."

After a pause, she said, "I dunnut understand that; you've no house, nor no brass, I guess?"

"The want of house or brass (by which I suppose you mean money) does not make a beggar in your sense of the word."

"Are you book-learned?" she inquired, presently.

"Yes, very."

She opened her eyes wide. "Whatever cannot ye keep yourself for, then?"

"I have kept myself; and, I trust, shall keep myself again. What are you going to do with these gooseberries?" I inquired, as she brought out a basket of the fruit.

"Mak' 'em into pies."

"Give them to me and I'll pick them."

She consented; and she even brought me a clean towel to spread over my dress. "Ye've not been used to sarvant's wark, I see by your hands," she remarked. "Happen ye've been a dressmaker."

"No, you are wrong. And, now, never mind what I have been; tell me the name of this house."

"Some calls it Marsh End, and some calls it Moor House."

"And the gentleman who lives here is called Mr. St. John?"

"Nay; St. John is his kirstened name; his full name is Mr. St. John Rivers. And he doesn't live here; he is only staying a while with his sisters. When he is at his own home, he is in his own parish at Morton, a few miles off."

"And what is he?"

"He is a parson."

"This, then, is his father's residence?"

"Aye; but old Mr. Rivers died three weeks sin' of a stroke. Their mother has been dead this mony a year."

"Have you lived with the family long?"

"Thirty year. I nursed them all three."

"That proves you must have been an honest and faithful servant. I will say so much for you, though you have had the incivility to call me a beggar."

She again regarded me with a surprised stare. "I believe," she said, "I was quite mista'en in my thoughts of you; but there is so mony cheats goes about, you mun forgie me. I've clear a different notion on you now to what I had; you look a raight down dacent little crater."

"That will do—I forgive you now. Shake hands."

She put her floury and horny hand into mine; a smile illumined her rough face, and from that moment we were friends.

Hannah was evidently fond of talking. While I picked the fruit, and she made the paste for the pies, she told me that Mrs. Rivers had been a great reader, and studied a deal; and the "bairns" had taken after her. They had liked learning, all three, almost from the time they could speak. Mr. St. John, when he grew up, would go to college and be a parson; and the girls, as soon as they left school, would seek places as governesses. They had lived very little at home for a long while, and were only come now to stay a few weeks on account of their father's death; but they did so like Marsh End and Morton, and all these moors and hills about. They had been in London, and many other grand towns, but they always said there was no place like home.

Having finished my task of gooseberry picking, I asked where the two ladies and their brother were now.

Gone over to Morton for a walk, she said, but they would be back in half an hour to tea.

They returned within the time Hannah had allotted them; they entered by the kitchen door. Mr. St. John, when he saw me, merely bowed and passed through; the two ladies stopped. Mary kindly and calmly expressed the pleasure she felt in seeing me well enough to be able to come down; Diana took my hand. She shook her head at me.

"You should have waited for my leave to descend," she said. "You still look very pale—and so thin! Poor girl!"

Diana had a voice like the cooing of a dove. Her whole face seemed to me full of charm. Mary's features were equally pretty, but her expression was more reserved. Diana looked and spoke with a certain authority; she had a will, evidently.

"And what business have you here?" she continued. "It is not your place. Mary and I sit in the kitchen sometimes, because at home we like to be free, but you are a visitor, and must go into the parlor." Still holding my hand, she led me into the inner room. "Sit there," she said, placing me on the sofa, "while we get the tea ready; it is another privilege we exercise in our little moorland home—to prepare our own meals when we are so inclined."

She closed the door, leaving me with Mr. St. John, who sat opposite, a book in his hand. I examined, first, the parlor, and then its occupant.

The parlor was small, plainly furnished, yet comfortable, because clean and neat. The old-fashioned chairs were very bright, and the walnut-wood table was like a looking glass. Everything—including the carpet and curtains—looked at once well worn and well saved.

Mr. St. John, keeping his eyes fixed on the page he perused, was easy enough to examine. He was young—perhaps twenty-eight—tall, slender; his face riveted the eye; it was like a Greek face, very pure in outline. His eyes were large and blue, with brown lashes; his high forehead, colorless as ivory, was partially streaked over by careless locks of fair hair. This is a gentle delineation, is it not, reader? Yet he whom it describes scarcely impressed one with the idea of a gentle nature. There was something about his nostril, his mouth, his brow, which indicated elements within either restless, or hard, or eager.

He did not speak to me one word till his sisters returned. Diana, in the course of preparing tea, brought me a little cake, baked on the top of the oven. "Eat that now," she said. "Hannah says you have had nothing but gruel since breakfast."

I did not refuse it, for my appetite was awakened and keen. Mr. Rivers now closed his book, approached the table, and, as he took a seat, fixed his blue eyes full on me. There was an unceremonious directness in his gaze.

"You are very hungry," he said.

"I am, sir."

"It is well for you that a low fever has forced you to abstain for the last three days; there would have been danger in yielding to the cravings of your appetite at first. Now you may eat, though still not immoderately."

"I trust I shall not eat long at your expense, sir," was my very clumsily contrived answer.

"No," he said, coolly. "When you have indicated to us the residence of your friends, we can write to them, and you may be restored to home."

"That, I must plainly tell you, is out of my power to do, being absolutely without home and friends."

The three looked at me. "Do you mean to say," St. John asked, "that you are completely isolated from every connection?"

"I do."

"A most singular position at your age!"

Here I saw his glance directed to my hands. I wondered what

he sought there; his words soon explained the quest. "You have never been married?"

Diana laughed. "Why, she can't be above seventeen or eighteen, St. John," she said.

"I am near nineteen, but I am not married. No."

I felt a burning glow mount to my face, for bitter and agitating recollections were awakened by the allusion to marriage. Diana and Mary relieved me by turning their eyes elsewhere than to my crimsoned visage, but the colder and sterner brother continued to gaze.

"Where did you last reside?" he now asked.

"You are too inquisitive, St. John," murmured Mary; but he leaned over the table and required an answer, by a second firm and piercing look.

"The name of the place where, and of the person with whom I lived, is my secret," I replied, concisely.

"Which you have, in my opinion, a right to keep, both from St. John and every other questioner," remarked Diana.

"Yet if I know nothing about you or your history, I cannot help you," he said. "And you need help, do you not?"

"I need it, and I seek it; so far, sir, that some true philanthropist will put me in the way of getting work which I can do, and the remuneration for which will keep me."

"I know not whether I am a true philanthropist; yet I am willing to aid you to the utmost of my power, in a purpose so honest. First, then, tell me what you *can* do."

I had now swallowed my tea. I was mightily refreshed by the beverage; it enabled me to address this penetrating young judge steadily. "Mr. Rivers," I said, turning to him, "you and your sisters have rescued me from death. This gives you an unlimited claim on my gratitude; and a claim, to a certain extent, on my confidence. I will tell you as much as I can without compromising my own peace of mind—my own security, moral and physical, and that of others.

"I am an orphan, the daughter of a clergyman. My parents died before I could know them. I was brought up a dependent;

educated in a charitable institution, Lowood Orphan Asylum, ——shire; you will have heard of it, Mr. Rivers?"

"I have seen the school."

"I left Lowood nearly a year since to become a private governess. I obtained a good situation, and was happy. This place I was obliged to leave four days before I came here. The reason of my departure I cannot explain: it would be useless—dangerous—and would sound incredible. No blame attached to me; I am as free from culpability as any one of you three. Miserable I am, and must be for a time; for the catastrophe which drove me from the house was of a direful nature. I observed but two points in planning my departure—speed, secrecy. To secure these, I had to leave behind me everything I possessed except a small parcel, which, in my trouble of mind, I forgot to take out of the coach that brought me to Whitcross. To this neighborhood, then, I came, quite destitute. I wandered about two days without crossing a threshold; it was when brought by hunger, exhaustion and despair, almost to the last gasp, that you, Mr. Rivers, took me under your roof. I know all your sisters have done for me since, and I owe to their compassion as large a debt as to your charity."

"Don't make her talk anymore now, St. John," said Diana, as I paused; "she is evidently not yet fit for excitement. Come to the sofa, and sit down now, Miss Elliott."

I gave an involuntary start at hearing the alias: I had forgotten my new name. Mr. Rivers noticed it at once.

"You said your name was Jane Elliott?" he observed.

"I did say so; and it is the name by which I think it expedient to be called at present. It is not my real name; I fear discovery above all things."

"You are quite right, I am sure," said Diana. "Now do, brother, let her be at peace awhile."

But when St. John had mused a few moments, he recommenced, as imperturbably as ever. "You would not like to be long dependent on our hospitality—you would wish, I see, to dispense as soon as may be with my sisters' compassion; and, above all, with my *charity* (I am quite sensible of the distinction drawn, nor do I resent it—it is just): you desire to be independent of us?"

"I do so wish. Show me how to work, or how to seek work: that is all I now ask; then let me go, if it be but to the meanest cottage—but till then, allow me to stay here."

"Indeed, you *shall* stay here," said Diana.

"You *shall*," repeated Mary, in a tone of sincerity.

"My sisters, you see, have a pleasure in keeping you," said Mr. St. John. "*I* feel more inclination to put you in the way of keeping yourself, and shall endeavor to do so; but I am but the incumbent of a poor country parish: my aid must be of the humblest sort."

"She has already said that she is willing to do anything honest she *can* do," answered Diana, for me.

"I will be a dressmaker; I will be a plain-work woman; I will be a servant, a nurse girl, if I can be no better," I answered.

"Right," said Mr. St. John, quite coolly. "If such is your spirit, I promise to aid you, in my own time and way."

He now resumed the book with which he had been occupied before tea. I soon withdrew; for I had talked as much, and sat up as long, as my present strength would permit.

CHAPTER XVI

THE MORE I KNEW OF THE INMATES of Moor House, the better I liked them. In a few days I had so far recovered my health that I could join with Diana and Mary in all their occupations; there was a reviving pleasure in this intercourse—the pleasure arising from perfect congeniality of tastes, sentiments and principles.

If in our trio there was a superior and a leader, it was Diana. Physically, she far excelled me: she was handsome; she was vigorous. I could talk a while when the evening commenced; but the first gush of vivacity and fluency gone, I was fain to sit on a stool at Diana's feet, and listen alternately to her and Mary, while they sounded thoroughly the topic on which I had but touched. They

discovered I could draw: their pencils and color boxes were immediately at my service. My skill, greater in this one point than theirs, surprised and charmed them.

As to Mr. St. John, the intimacy which had arisen so naturally between me and his sisters did not extend to him. One reason was that he was comparatively seldom at home: a large proportion of his time appeared devoted to visiting the sick and poor among the scattered population of his parish. But besides his frequent absences, there was another barrier to friendship with him: he seemed of a reserved, even of a brooding nature. Zealous in his ministerial labors, blameless in his life and habits, he yet did not appear to enjoy that mental serenity, that inward content which should be the reward of every sincere Christian.

Meantime a month was gone. Diana and Mary were soon to leave Moor House, and return to the far different life which awaited them, as governesses in a large, fashionable, south-of-England city. Mr. St. John had said nothing to me yet about the employment he had promised to obtain for me; yet it became urgent that I should have a vocation of some kind. One morning, being left alone with him a few minutes in the parlor, I ventured to approach him, though not very well knowing in what words to frame my inquiry. He looked up as I drew near. "You have a question?" he said.

"Yes; I wish to know whether you have heard of any service I can offer myself to undertake."

"I found something for you three weeks ago; but as you seemed both useful and happy here I deemed it inexpedient to break in on your comfort till my sisters' departure from Marsh End."

"What is the employment you had in view, Mr. Rivers?"

He seemed reluctant to continue. "Let me frankly tell you, I have nothing profitable to suggest. Since I am myself poor and obscure, I can offer you but a service of poverty and obscurity."

"Well?" I said, as he again paused. "Do explain."

"I will; and you shall hear how poor the proposal is. Morton, when I came to it two years ago, had no school. I established one for boys; I mean now to open a second school for girls. I have hired a building for the purpose, with a cottage of two rooms attached to it for the mistress's house. Her salary will be thirty pounds a year; her house is already furnished by the kindness of a lady, Miss Oliver, the only daughter of the sole rich man in my parish, the proprietor of a needle factory and iron foundry in the valley. The same lady pays for the education and clothing of an orphan from the workhouse, on condition that she shall aid the mistress in such menial offices as her occupation of teaching will prevent her having time to discharge in person. Will you be this mistress?"

He put the question rather hurriedly; he seemed half to expect a rejection of the offer. In truth it was humble—but it was not ignoble—not unworthy. I made my decision.

"I thank you for the proposal, Mr. Rivers; and I accept it with all my heart."

"You know what you undertake, then?"

"I do."

He now smiled, as one well pleased and gratified.

"And when will you commence the exercise of your function?"

"I will go to my house tomorrow, and open the school, if you like, next week."

"Very well; so be it."

DIANA AND MARY RIVERS became more sad and silent as the day approached for leaving their brother and their home. Diana intimated that this would be a different parting from any they had ever yet known. It would probably, as far as St. John was concerned, be a parting for years; it might be a parting for life.

"He will sacrifice all to his long-framed resolves," she said. "St. John looks quiet, Jane; but he hides a fever in his vitals. You would think him gentle, yet in some things he is inexorable as death. His decision is right, noble, Christian, yet it breaks my heart."

And the tears gushed to her fine eyes. Mary bent her head low over her work. "We are now without father; we shall soon be without home and brother," she murmured.

At that moment a little incident supervened. St. John passed the window reading a letter. He entered.

"Our Uncle John is dead," said he.

Both the sisters seemed struck, not shocked or appalled; the tidings appeared in their eyes rather momentous than afflicting.

Diana riveted a searching gaze on her brother's face. "And what then?" she demanded, in a low voice.

"What then, Diana?" he replied, maintaining a marble immobility of feature. "What then? Why—nothing. Read."

He threw the letter into her lap. She glanced over it, and handed it to Mary. All three looked at each other, and all three smiled—a dreary, pensive smile enough.

"At any rate, it makes us no worse off than we were before," remarked Mary.

"Only it forces rather strongly on the mind the picture of what *might have been*," said Mr. Rivers, "and contrasts it somewhat too vividly with what *is*."

He folded the letter, and locked it in his desk, and again went out. For some minutes no one spoke. Diana then turned to me.

"Jane, you will wonder at us," she said; "and think us hard-hearted beings not to be more moved at the death of so near a relation as an uncle; but we have never known him. He was my mother's brother. My father and he quarreled long ago. It was by his advice that my father risked most of his property in the speculation that ruined him; they parted in anger, and were never reconciled.

"My uncle engaged afterwards in more prosperous undertakings; it appears he realized a fortune of twenty thousand pounds. He was never married and had no near kindred but ourselves, and one other person, not more closely related than we. My father always cherished the idea that he would atone for his error by leaving his possessions to us; that letter informs us that he has bequeathed every penny to the other relation. He had a right, of course, to do as he pleased; yet the receipt of such news causes a momentary damp to the spirit. Mary and I would have esteemed ourselves rich with a thousand pounds each; and to St. John such a sum would have been valuable for the good it would have enabled him to do."

This explanation given, the subject was dropped, and no further reference made to it.

The next day, I left Marsh End for Morton. The day after, Diana and Mary quitted it for distant B——. In a week Mr. Rivers and Hannah repaired to the parsonage; and so the old grange was abandoned.

MY HOME, THEN—when I at last find a home—is a cottage: a little room with whitewashed walls, containing four painted chairs and a table, a clock, a cupboard, and a set of tea things in delft. Above, a chamber of the same dimensions, with a deal bedstead and chest of drawers.

It is evening. I have dismissed, with an orange, the little orphan who serves me as a handmaid. I am sitting alone on the hearth. This morning, the village school opened. I had twenty scholars. But three of the number can read; none write or cipher. They speak with the broadest accent of the district. Some of them are unmannered, rough, intractable, as well as ignorant; but others have a wish to learn. I must not forget that the germs of refinement, intelligence, kind feeling, are as likely to exist in the hearts of these little peasants as in those of the best-born. My duty will be to develop these germs; surely I shall find some happiness in discharging that office.

Much enjoyment I do not expect in the life opening before me, yet it will, doubtless, yield me enough to live on from day to day.

Having brought my eventide musings to this point, I rose, went to my door, and looked at the sunset and at the quiet fields before my cottage, which, with the school, was distant half a mile from the village. While I looked, I thought myself happy, and was surprised to find myself ere long weeping—and why? For the doom which had reft me from my master; for him I was no more to see. I hid my eyes, and leaned my head against the stone frame of my door; but soon a slight noise near the wicket which shut in my tiny garden made me look up. A dog—old Carlo, Mr. Rivers' pointer—was pushing the gate with his nose, and St. John himself leaned upon it with folded arms. I asked him to come in.

"No, I cannot stay; I have only brought you a little parcel my sisters left for you. I think it contains a color box and paper."

I approached to take it; a welcome gift it was. He examined my face as I came near. "Have you found your first day's work harder than you expected?" he asked.

"Oh, no! On the contrary, I think in time I shall get on with my scholars very well. All I see has made me thankful, not despondent. I wonder at the goodness of God, and the bounty of my lot."

"But you feel solitude an oppression?"

"I have hardly had time yet to feel loneliness."

"Very well. I hope you feel the content you express. What you had left before I saw you, of course I do not know; but I counsel you to resist, firmly, every temptation which would incline you to look back; pursue your present career steadily, for some months at least."

"It is what I mean to do," I answered.

St. John continued: "It is hard work to control the workings of inclination, and turn the bent of nature; but that it may be done, I know from experience. A year ago, I was myself intensely miserable, because I thought I had made a mistake in entering the ministry: its uniform duties wearied me to death. I burned for the more active life of the world—for the destiny of a soldier, politician, orator; anything rather than that of a priest. After a season of darkness and struggling, light broke. God had an errand for

me; to bear which afar, to deliver it well, skill and strength, courage and eloquence, the best qualifications of soldier, statesman
and orator, were all needed: for these all center in the good
missionary.

"A missionary I resolved to be. My father, indeed, opposed the
determination, but since his death, I have not a legitimate obstacle
to contend with; some affairs settled, a successor for Morton provided, an entanglement or two of the feelings cut asunder—and
I leave Europe for the East."

He said this, in his subdued, yet emphatic voice, looking, when
he had ceased speaking, not at me, but at the setting sun. Both he
and I had our backs towards the path leading up the field to the
wicket. We had heard no step on that grass-grown track; we might
well then start, when a gay voice exclaimed:

"Good evening, Mr. Rivers. And good evening, old Carlo.
Your dog is quicker to recognize his friends than you are, sir; he
pricked his ears and wagged his tail when I was at the bottom of
the field, and you have your back towards me now."

It was true. Though Mr. Rivers had started at the first of those
musical accents, as if a thunderbolt had split a cloud over his
head, he stood yet in the same attitude in which the speaker had
surprised him—his face directed towards the west. He turned at
last, with measured deliberation. There appeared, within three feet
of him, a form clad in pure white—a youthful, graceful form.
When, after bending to caress Carlo, it lifted up its head, there
bloomed under his glance a face of perfect beauty.

What did St. John Rivers think of this earthly angel? He had
already withdrawn his eye from her, and was looking at a humble
tuft of daisies which grew by the wicket.

"A lovely evening, but late for you to be out alone," he said,
as he crushed the snowy heads of the closed flowers with his foot.

"Oh, I only came home from S—— this afternoon. Papa told me
you had opened your school, and that the new mistress was come;
and so I have run up the valley to see her. This is she?" pointing
to me.

"It is," said St. John.

"Do you think you shall like Morton?" she asked of me, with a direct and naïve simplicity of tone and manner.

"I hope I shall. I have many inducements to do so."

"Did you find your scholars as attentive as you expected?"

"Quite."

"Have I furnished your house nicely?"

"Very nicely indeed." This, then, I thought, is Miss Oliver, the heiress.

"I shall come up and help you to teach sometimes," she added. "Mr. Rivers, I have been *so* gay during my stay at S——. Last night, or rather this morning, I was dancing till two o'clock. The —th regiment are stationed there; and the officers are the most agreeable men in the world."

It seemed to me that Mr. St. John's under lip protruded, and his upper lip curled a moment. He lifted his gaze, too, from the daisies, and turned it on her. An unsmiling, a searching, a meaning gaze it was. As he stood, mute and grave, she again fell to caressing Carlo. "Poor Carlo loves me," said she. "*He* is not stern and distant to his friends; and if he could speak, he would not be silent."

As she patted the dog's head, bending with native grace before his young and austere master, I saw a glow rise to that master's face. I saw his solemn eye melt with sudden fire, and flicker with resistless emotion. But he curbed the emotion, I think, as a resolute rider would curb a rearing steed.

"Papa says you never come to see us now," continued Miss Oliver. "He is alone this evening; will you return with me and visit him?"

"It is not a seasonable hour to intrude on Mr. Oliver," answered St. John.

"Not a seasonable hour! It is just the hour when Papa most wants company: when he has no business to occupy him. Mr. Rivers, *do* come. Why are you so very shy, and so very somber?" She filled up the hiatus his silence left by a reply of her own. "I forgot!" she exclaimed, shaking her beautiful curled head, as if shocked at herself. "I am thoughtless! *Do* excuse me. It had slipped my memory that you have good reasons to be indisposed for joining in my chatter. Diana and Mary have left you, and Moor House is shut up, and you are so lonely. I am sure I pity you. Do come and see Papa."

"Not tonight, Miss Rosamond, not tonight."

"Well, if you are so obstinate, I will leave you, for I dare not stay any longer: the dew begins to fall. Good evening!"

She held out her hand. He just touched it. "Good evening!" he repeated, in a voice low and hollow as an echo. She turned, but in a moment returned. "Are you well?" she asked. Well might she put the question: his face was blanched as her gown.

"Quite well," he enunciated; and, with a bow, he left the gate. She went one way, he another. She turned twice to gaze after him as she tripped fairylike down the field; he, as he strode firmly across, never turned at all.

This spectacle of another's suffering and sacrifice rapt my thoughts from exclusive meditation on my own. Diana had designated her brother "inexorable as death." She had not exaggerated.

CHAPTER XVII

I CONTINUED THE LABORS OF THE VILLAGE SCHOOL as actively and faithfully as I could. Some time elapsed before, with all my efforts, I could comprehend my scholars and their nature. Wholly untaught, with faculties quite torpid, they seemed to me hopelessly dull, but I soon found I was mistaken. Their amazement at me, my language, my rules and ways, once subsided, I found some of these heavy-looking, gaping rustics wake up into sharp-witted girls enough. Many showed themselves obliging, and amiable too; and I discovered amongst them not a few examples of natural politeness and innate self-respect, as well as of excellent capacity, that won my goodwill and my admiration.

I felt I became a favorite in the neighborhood. Whenever I went out, I was welcomed with friendly smiles. To live amidst general regard is like "sitting in sunshine, calm and sweet." At this period of my life, my heart far oftener swelled with thankfulness than

sank with dejection; and yet, reader, in the midst of this calm—
after a day passed in honorable exertion among my scholars, an
evening spent in drawing or reading contentedly alone—I used to
rush into strange dreams at night, where I again and again met
Mr. Rochester, always at some exciting crisis; and then the sense of
being in his arms, hearing his voice, loving him, being loved by
him—the hope of passing a lifetime at his side, would be renewed,
with all its first force and fire. Then I awoke. Then I recalled
where I was, and how situated; and then the still, dark night witnessed the convulsion of despair, and heard the burst of passion.
By nine o'clock the next morning I was punctually opening the
school, tranquil, settled, prepared for the steady duties of the day.

Rosamond Oliver kept her word in coming to the school, and
she also honored me with frequent visits to my cottage. I had
learned her whole character, which was without mystery or disguise. She had been indulged from her birth, but was not absolutely spoilt. She was hasty, but good-humored; vain, but not
affected; gay, lively and unthinking. She was very charming, in
short, even to a cool observer of her own sex like me.

One evening, while, with her usual childlike activity, and
thoughtless yet not offensive inquisitiveness, she was rummaging
the table drawer of my little kitchen, she discovered my drawing
materials and some sketches, including a pencil-head of a pretty
little girl, one of my scholars, and sundry views from nature. She
was electrified with delight. Had I done these pictures? I drew
better than her master in her school. Would I sketch a portrait of
her, to show to Papa?

"With pleasure," I replied; and I felt a thrill of artist-delight at
the idea of copying from so perfect and radiant a model. She had
then on a dark blue silk dress; her only ornament was her chestnut
tresses, which waved in curls over her shoulders. I took a sheet of
fine cardboard, and drew a careful outline. I promised myself the
pleasure of coloring it; and, as it was getting late then, I told her
she must come and sit another day.

She made such a report of me to her father that Mr. Oliver himself accompanied her next evening—a tall, massive-featured, gray-

headed man. The sketch of Rosamond's portrait pleased him highly. He insisted, too, on my coming the next day to spend the evening at Vale Hall.

I went; Rosamond was full of pleasure; her father was affable; and at tea he expressed in strong terms his approbation of what I had done in Morton school. He also spoke of Mr. Rivers with great respect. He said it was a very old name in that neighborhood; that even now he considered the representative of that house might, if he liked, make an alliance with the best. He accounted it a pity that so fine and talented a young man should have formed the design of going out as a missionary; it was quite throwing a valuable life away. It appeared, then, that her father would throw no obstacle in the way of Rosamond's union with St. John.

On the fifth of November, a holiday, I had the afternoon to spend as I would, and I got my palette and pencils, and fell to completing Rosamond Oliver's miniature. The head was finished already; there was but the background to tint, and the drapery to shade off. I was absorbed in the execution of these nice details when, after one rapid tap, my door unclosed, admitting St. John Rivers.

"I am come to see how you are spending your holiday," he said. "Not, I hope, in thought? No, that is well: while you draw you will not feel lonely. I have brought you a book for evening solace," and he laid on the table a new publication—a poem. While I was eagerly glancing at the bright pages of *Marmion* (for *Marmion* it was), St.

John stooped to examine my drawing. His tall figure sprang erect again with a start; he said nothing. I looked up at him; he shunned my eye. I knew his thoughts well, and could read his heart plainly; at the moment I felt calmer and cooler than he, and I conceived an inclination to do him some good, if I could; I was sure it would benefit him to talk a little about this sweet Rosamond Oliver.

"Is this portrait like?" I asked bluntly.

"Like? Like whom? I did not observe it closely."

"You did, Mr. Rivers."

He started at my strange abruptness. I continued, "You observed it closely; but I have no objection to your looking at it again," and I rose and placed it in his hand.

"A well-executed picture," he said; "very graceful."

"Yes, yes; I know. But what of the resemblance? Who is it like?"

Mastering some hesitation, he answered, "Miss Oliver, I presume."

"Of course. And now, sir, to reward you for the accurate guess, I will promise to paint you a faithful duplicate of this very picture, provided you admit that the gift would be acceptable to you."

He continued to gaze at the picture; the longer he looked, the more he seemed to covet it. "It is like!" he murmured; "the eye is well managed; the color, light, expression, are perfect. It smiles!"

"Would it comfort, or would it wound you to have a similar painting? When you are at Madagascar, or at the Cape, or in India, would it be a consolation to have that memento?"

He raised his eyes. "That I should like to have it, is certain; whether it would be judicious or wise is another question."

Since I had ascertained that Rosamond really preferred him, and that her father was not likely to oppose the match, I—less exalted in my views than St. John—had been strongly disposed in my own heart to advocate their union.

"As far as I can see, it would be wiser and more judicious if you were to take to yourself the original at once."

By this time he had sat down. I discerned he was now neither angry nor shocked at my audacity. I saw even that to be thus frankly addressed on a subject he had deemed unapproachable was beginning to be felt by him as a new pleasure, an unhoped-for relief.

"She likes you," said I, "and her father respects you."

"*Does* she like me?" he asked.

"Certainly; she talks of you continually. There is no subject she enjoys so much."

"It is very pleasant to hear this," he said, "very. Go on for another quarter of an hour." And he actually took out his watch and laid it upon the table to measure the time.

"But where is the use of going on," I asked, "when you are probably forging a fresh chain to fetter your heart?"

"Don't imagine such hard things. Fancy me yielding and melting, as I am doing: human love rising like a fresh fountain in my mind. Hush! say nothing—I think of Rosamond—my heart is full of delight—my senses are entranced—let the time I marked pass in peace."

I humored him; the watch ticked on. I stood silent. Amidst this hush the quarter sped; then he replaced the watch.

"Now," said he, "that little space was given to delirium and delusion. It is strange that while I love Rosamond Oliver so wildly I experience at the same time a calm consciousness that she would not make me a good wife; that I should discover this within a year after marriage; and that to twelve months' rapture would succeed a lifetime of regret. This I know."

"Strange, indeed!" I could not help ejaculating.

"Her defects are such that she could cooperate in nothing I undertook. Rosamond a missionary's wife? No!"

"But you need not be a missionary. You might relinquish that scheme."

"Relinquish! What! My vocation? My hopes of being numbered in the band who have merged all ambitions in the glorious one of carrying knowledge into the realms of ignorance? Must I relinquish that? It is dearer than the blood in my veins."

After a considerable pause, I said, "And Miss Oliver? Are her disappointment and sorrow of no interest to you?"

"Miss Oliver is ever surrounded by suitors. In less than a month, my image will be effaced from her heart. She will marry, probably, someone who will make her far happier than I should do."

"You speak coolly enough, but you suffer in the conflict. You are wasting away."

"No. If I get a little thin, it is with anxiety about my prospects. Only this morning I received intelligence that my successor cannot be ready to replace me for three months to come yet, and perhaps the three months may extend to six. No; know me to be what I am—a cold, hard man. Reason, and not Feeling, is my guide; my ambition is unlimited; my desire to rise higher, to do more than others, insatiable."

Having said this he took his hat, which lay on the table beside my palette. Once more he looked at the portrait.

"She *is* lovely," he murmured. "She is well named the Rose of the World, indeed!"

"And may I not paint one like it for you?"

"*Cui bono?* No."

He drew over the picture the sheet of thin paper on which I was accustomed to rest my hand in painting, to prevent the cardboard from being sullied. What he suddenly saw on this blank paper, I could not tell, but he took it up with a snatch; he looked at the edge, then shot a glance at me, quite incomprehensible.

"What is the matter?" I asked.

"Nothing in the world," was the reply, and, replacing the paper, I saw him dexterously tear a slip from the margin. It disappeared in his glove; and, with a hasty "Good afternoon," he vanished.

"Well!" I exclaimed, using an expression of the district, "that caps the globe!"

I, in my turn, scrutinized the paper; but saw nothing on it save a few stains of paint. I pondered the mystery a minute or two; but finding it insolvable, I soon forgot it.

When Mr. St. John went, it was beginning to snow; the whirling storm continued all night. The next day brought fresh falls; by twilight the valley was drifted up and almost impassable. I had closed my shutter, laid a mat to the door to prevent the snow from blowing in under it, and trimmed my fire. After lighting a candle, I took down *Marmion* and soon forgot storm in music. Then I heard a noise; it was St. John Rivers, who, lifting the latch, came in out of the darkness, his cloak white as a glacier. I was almost in consternation, so little had I expected any guest. "Any ill news?" I demanded. "Has anything happened?"

"No. How very easily alarmed you are!" he answered, stamping the snow from his boots.

"Why are you come?" I could not forbear saying.

"Rather an inhospitable question; but since you ask it, I answer, simply to have a little talk with you. Besides, since yesterday, I have experienced the excitement of a person to whom a tale has been half told, and who is impatient to hear the sequel."

He sat down. I recalled his singular conduct of yesterday, and really I began to fear his wits were touched. I waited, hoping he would say something I could at least comprehend; but his hand was now at his chin; his eye dwelt dreamily on the glowing grate; he was thinking.

"Come a little nearer the fire," he said at last.

Wondering, I complied.

"When I arrived," he pursued, "I spoke of my impatience to hear the sequel of a tale. On reflection, I find the matter will be better managed by my assuming the narrator's part, and converting you into a listener.

"Twenty years ago, a poor curate—never mind his name at this moment—fell in love with a rich man's daughter; she fell in love with him, and married him, against the advice of all her friends, who consequently disowned her after the wedding. Before two years passed, the rash pair were both dead, and laid quietly side by side under one slab. They left a daughter, whom Charity received in her lap. Charity carried the friendless thing to the house of its rich, maternal relations; it was reared by an aunt-in-law, called (I come to names now) Mrs. Reed of Gateshead—you start—did you hear a noise? I daresay it is only a rat scrambling along the rafters of the adjoining schoolroom. To proceed. Mrs. Reed kept the orphan ten years. Whether it was happy or not with her, I cannot say, but at the end of that time she transferred it to a place you know—being no other than Lowood school, where you so long resided yourself.

"It seems her career there was very honorable: from a pupil, she became a teacher, like yourself—really it strikes me there are parallel points in her history and yours—she left it to be a governess. There, again, your fates were analogous; she undertook the education of the ward of a certain Mr. Rochester."

"Mr. Rivers!" I interrupted.

"I can guess your feelings," he said, "but I have nearly finished; hear me to the end. Of Mr. Rochester's character I know nothing but the one fact that he professed to offer honorable marriage to this young girl, and that at the very altar she discovered he had a wife yet alive, though a lunatic. What his subsequent conduct and proposals were is a matter of pure conjecture; but when an event transpired which rendered inquiry after the governess necessary, it was discovered she was gone. She had left Thornfield Hall in the night; every search after her course had been vain; no vestige of information could be gathered respecting her. Yet that she should be found is become a matter of serious urgency: advertisements have been put in all the papers; I myself have received a letter from one Mr. Briggs, a solicitor, communicating the details I have just imparted. Is it not an odd tale?"

"Just tell me this," said I, "and since you know so much, you surely *can* tell me—what of Mr. Rochester? How and where is he? Is he well?"

"I am ignorant of all concerning Mr. Rochester; the letter never mentions him but to narrate the fraudulent attempt I have adverted to. You should rather ask the name of the governess—the nature of the event which requires her appearance."

"Did no one go to Thornfield Hall then? Did no one see Mr. Rochester?"

"I suppose not."

"But they wrote to him?"

"Of course."

"And what did he say? Who has his letters?"

"Mr. Briggs intimates that the answer to his application was not from Mr. Rochester, but from a lady; it is signed 'Alice Fairfax.'"

I felt cold and dismayed. My worst fears then were probably true: he had in all probability left England and rushed in desperation to some former haunt on the Continent. Oh, my poor master!

"He must have been a bad man," observed Mr. Rivers.

"You don't know him—don't pronounce an opinion upon him," I said, with warmth.

"Very well," he answered, quietly, "and indeed my head is otherwise occupied than with him: I have my tale to finish. Since you won't ask the governess's name, I must tell it of my own accord—stay—I have it here."

His pocketbook was produced, opened; from one of its compartments was extracted a shabby slip of paper. I recognized in its texture and its stains of ultramarine the ravished margin of the portrait cover. He got up, held it close to my eyes; and I read, in my own handwriting, the words JANE EYRE—the work doubtless of some moment of abstraction.

"Briggs wrote to me of a Jane Eyre," he said; "I knew a Jane Elliott. I confess I had my suspicions, but it was only yesterday afternoon they were at once resolved into certainty. You own the name and renounce the alias?"

"Yes—yes—but where is Mr. Briggs? He perhaps knows more of Mr. Rochester than you do."

"Briggs is in London. I should doubt his knowing anything at all about Mr. Rochester; it is not in Mr. Rochester he is interested. Meantime, you forget essential points in pursuing trifles: you do not inquire why Mr. Briggs sought after you."

"Well, what did he want?"

"Merely to tell you that your uncle, Mr. Eyre of Madeira, is dead; that he has left you all his property. You are now rich."

"I! Rich?"

"Yes, you, rich—quite an heiress."

Silence succeeded.

"You must prove your identity, of course," resumed St. John

presently, "a step which will offer no difficulties; you can then enter on immediate possession."

Here was a new card turned up! It is a fine thing, reader, to be lifted in a moment from indigence to wealth—a very fine thing; but not a matter one can comprehend, or consequently enjoy, all at once. Besides, the words legacy, bequest, go side by side with the words death, funeral. My uncle I had heard was dead—my only relative; ever since being made aware of his existence, I had cherished the hope of one day seeing him; now, I never should. And then this money came only to me: not to me and a rejoicing family, but to my isolated self. It was a grand boon, doubtless, and independence would be glorious—yes, I felt *that*.

"You unbend your forehead at last," said Mr. Rivers. "I thought that you were turning to stone—perhaps now you will ask how much you are worth?"

"How much am I worth?"

"Oh, a trifle! Nothing of course to speak of—twenty thousand pounds, I think they say—but what is that?"

"Twenty thousand pounds?"

Here was a new stunner—I had been calculating on four or five thousand. This news actually took my breath for a moment. Mr. St. John, whom I had never heard laugh before, laughed now.

"Well," said he, "if you had committed a murder, and I had told you your crime was discovered, you could scarcely look more aghast."

"It is a large sum."

Mr. Rivers rose and put his cloak on. "If it were not such a wild night," he said, "I would send Hannah down to keep you company: you look too desperately miserable to be left alone. But Hannah, poor woman, could not stride the drifts so well as I, so I must e'en leave you to your sorrows. Good night."

He was lifting the latch. A sudden thought occurred to me.

"Stop one minute!" I cried. "It puzzles me to know why Mr. Briggs wrote to you about me."

"Oh, I am a clergyman," he said, "and the clergy are often appealed to about odd matters." Again the latch rattled.

"No; that does not satisfy me!" I exclaimed. "It is a very strange piece of business, and I must know more about it. You certainly shall not go till you have told me all!"

"I would rather not, just now."

"You shall! You must!"

"Well, then," he said, "I yield; if not to your earnestness, to your perseverance. Besides, you must know someday. Your name is Jane Eyre? You are not, perhaps, aware that I was christened St. John Eyre Rivers?"

"No, indeed! But what then? Surely—"

I stopped; I could not trust myself to entertain the thought that rushed upon me. Circumstances knit themselves, shot into order: I knew, by instinct, how the matter stood, before St. John had said another word.

"My mother's name was Eyre; she had two brothers—one a clergyman, who married Miss Jane Reed, of Gateshead; the other, John Eyre, Esquire, merchant, late of Madeira. Mr. Briggs, being Mr. Eyre's solicitor, wrote to us last August to inform us of our uncle's death; and to say that he had left his property to his brother the clergyman's orphan daughter, overlooking us, in consequence of a quarrel between him and my father. He wrote again a few weeks since, to intimate that the heiress was lost, and asking if we knew anything of her. A name casually written on a slip of paper has enabled me to find her out. You know the rest." Again he was going, but I set my back against the door.

"Do let me speak," I said; "let me have one moment to draw breath and reflect." I paused—he stood before me, hat in hand, looking composed enough. I resumed:

"Your mother was my father's sister? You three, then, are my cousins?"

"We are cousins; yes."

I surveyed him. It seemed I had found a brother: one I could be proud of, one I could love; and two sisters, whose qualities inspired me with genuine affection. Glorious discovery to a lonely wretch! This was wealth indeed! I clapped my hands in joy. "Oh, I am glad!" I exclaimed.

St. John smiled. "Did I not say you neglected essential points to pursue trifles? You were serious when I told you you had got a fortune; and now, for a matter of no moment, you are excited."

"What *can* you mean? It may be of no moment to you; you have sisters, but I had nobody; and now three relations—or two, if you don't choose to be counted—are born into my world full grown. I say again, I am glad!"

I walked fast through the room; I stopped, half suffocated with the thoughts that rose faster than I could receive, comprehend, settle them. Those who had saved my life, whom, till this hour, I had loved barrenly, I could now benefit. They were under a yoke; I could free them. Were we not four? Twenty thousand pounds, shared equally, would be five thousand each—enough and to spare; justice would be done, mutual happiness secured.

Now the wealth did not weigh on me—it was a legacy of life, hope, enjoyment.

"Write to Diana and Mary tomorrow," I said to Mr. Rivers, "and tell them to come home directly. Diana said they would both consider themselves rich with a thousand pounds, so with five thousand they will do very well."

"Tell me where I can get a glass of water," said St. John; "you must make an effort to tranquilize your feelings."

"Nonsense! And what effect will the bequest have on you? Will it keep you in England and induce you to marry Miss Oliver?"

"You wander; the news has excited you beyond your strength."

"Mr. Rivers! You quite put me out of patience; I am rational enough; it is you who misunderstand."

"Perhaps if you explained yourself a little more fully, I should comprehend better."

"Explain! What is there to explain? You cannot fail to see that twenty thousand pounds divided equally between the nephew and three nieces of our uncle will give five thousand to each? What I want is, that you should write to your sisters and tell them of the fortune that has accrued to them."

"To you, you mean."

"I have intimated my view of the case; I am incapable of taking any other. I am not brutally selfish, blindly unjust, or fiendishly ungrateful. Besides, I am resolved I will have a home and connections. I like Moor House, and I will live at Moor House. I like Diana and Mary, and I will attach myself to Diana and Mary. It would please me to have five thousand pounds; it would oppress me to have twenty thousand; which, moreover, could never be mine in justice, though it might in law."

"This is acting on first impulses; you must take days to consider such a matter ere your word can be regarded as valid."

"Oh, if all you doubt is my sincerity, I am easy. You see the justice of the case?"

"I *do* see a certain justice; but it is contrary to all custom. Besides, you do not know what it is to possess wealth; you cannot form a notion of the importance twenty thousand pounds would give you, of the prospects it would open to you—"

"And you," I interrupted, "cannot at all imagine the craving I have for fraternal and sisterly love. You will not be reluctant to own me, will you?"

"Jane: I will be your brother, my sisters will be your sisters, without stipulating for this sacrifice of your just rights. And indeed, your aspirations after family ties may be realized otherwise than by the means you contemplate: you may marry."

"Nonsense, again! Marry! I never shall marry. I do not want a stranger, I want my kindred. Say again you will be my brother; when you uttered the words I was happy; repeat them, if you can, sincerely."

"I think I can. I know I have always loved my own sisters; and I know on what my affection for them is grounded. Like them, you too have principle and mind; your presence is always agreeable to me. I feel I can easily make room in my heart for you."

"Thank you. That contents me for tonight. Now you had better go; for if you stay longer, you will perhaps irritate me afresh by some mistrustful scruple."

"And the school, Miss Eyre? It must now be shut up, I suppose?"

"No. I will retain my post of mistress till you get a substitute."

He smiled approbation; we shook hands, and he took leave.

I need not narrate in detail the further struggles I had to get matters regarding the legacy settled as I wished. My task was a hard one; but as my cousins saw at length that my mind was really and immutably fixed on making a just division of the property, the instruments of transfer were drawn up. St. John, Diana, Mary and I each became possessed of a competency.

CHAPTER XVIII

IT WAS NEAR CHRISTMAS BY THE TIME all was settled. I now closed Morton school. I had long felt with pleasure that many of my rustic scholars liked me, and when we parted that consciousness was confirmed: they manifested their affection plainly and strongly.

Mr. Rivers came up as—having seen the classes, now numbering sixty girls, file out before me, and locked the door—I stood with the key in my hand, exchanging a few words of special farewell with some half dozen of my best scholars.

"Do you consider you have got your reward for a season of exertion?" he asked when they were gone. "Does not the consciousness of having done some real good give pleasure?"

"Yes," I said; "but I could not go on forever so. I want to enjoy my own faculties as well as to cultivate those of other people. I must enjoy them now; I am out of school and disposed for full holiday."

He looked grave. "What sudden eagerness is this you evince? What are you going to do?"

"To be as active as I can. And first I must beg you to set Hannah at liberty. I want her to go with me to Moor House; Diana and Mary will be at home in a week, and I want to have everything in order against their arrival. My first aim will be to rub Moor House up with beeswax, oil, and an indefinite number of cloths, till it glitters again; and the last two days before your sisters are expected will be devoted by Hannah and me to such a beating of eggs, sorting of currants, grating of spices, and compounding of Christmas cakes and mince pies, as words can convey but an inadequate notion of to the uninitiated like you."

St. John smiled slightly. "It is all very well for the present," said he; "but seriously, I trust that when the first flush of vivacity is over you will look a little higher than domestic endearments and household joys."

I looked at him with surprise. "St. John," I said, "I think you are almost wicked to talk so. I am disposed to be as content as a queen and you try to stir me up to restlessness! I feel I have adequate cause to be happy, and I *will* be happy. Good-by!"

Happy at Moor House I was, and hard I worked; and so did Hannah. After a day or two of confusion worse confounded, it was delightful, by degrees, to invoke order from the chaos ourselves had made. I had previously taken a journey to S—— to purchase some new furniture, my cousins having given me carte blanche to effect what alterations I pleased, and a sum having been set aside for that purpose. Dark handsome new carpets and curtains, some carefully selected antique ornaments in porcelain and bronze, new coverings, and mirrors, and dressing cases for the toilet tables looked fresh without being glaring. I laid canvas on the passage, and carpets on the stairs. When all was finished, I thought Moor House as complete a model of bright modest snugness within as it was, at this season, a specimen of wintry waste and desert dreariness without.

The eventful Thursday at length came. They were expected about dark, and ere dusk, fires were lit upstairs and below; the kitchen was in perfect trim; Hannah and I were dressed and all was in readiness.

St. John arrived first. He found me in the kitchen, watching the progress of certain cakes then baking. Approaching the hearth, he asked if I was at last satisfied with housemaid's work. I answered by inviting him to accompany me on a general inspection of the result of my labors. He said I must have gone through a great deal of trouble, but not a syllable did he utter indicating pleasure in the improved aspect of his abode. This silence damped me. Reader, St. John was a good man; but I began to feel he had spoken truth of himself, when he said he was hard and cold. The humanities and amenities of life had no attraction for him. I saw he was of the material from which nature hews her heroes—a steadfast bulwark for great interests to rest upon; but, at the fireside, too often a cold cumbrous column, gloomy and out of place. Perhaps he had been right to choose a missionary's career.

"They are coming! They are coming!" cried Hannah at that moment, throwing open the parlor door. At the same moment old Carlo barked joyfully. Out I ran. The vehicle had stopped at the wicket; the driver opened the door. In a minute I had my face under their bonnets, in contact first with Mary's soft cheek, then with Diana's. They laughed—kissed me—then Hannah; patted Carlo, who was half wild with delight, and then hastened into the house.

Sweet was that evening. My cousins, full of exhilaration, were so eloquent that their fluency covered St. John's taciturnity; he was sincerely glad to see his sisters, but in their glow of fervor he could not sympathize. I saw he wished the quieter morrow was come. And I am afraid the whole of the ensuing week tried his patience. It was Christmas week and we spent it in a sort of merry domestic dissipation. St. John did not rebuke our vivacity, but he escaped from it: his parish was large, and he found daily business in visiting the sick and poor in it.

One morning, at breakfast, Diana, looking pensive, asked him if his plans were yet unchanged.

"Unchanged and unchangeable," was the reply. And he proceeded to inform us that his departure from England was now definitely fixed for the ensuing year.

"And Rosamond Oliver?" suggested Mary, the words seeming to escape her lips involuntarily; for no sooner had she uttered them, than she made a gesture as if wishing to recall them. St. John looked up.

"Rosamond Oliver," said he, "is about to be married to Mr. Granby, one of the best connected and most estimable residents in S——. I had the intelligence from her father yesterday."

The first time I found St. John alone at his desk after this communication, I felt tempted to inquire if the event distressed him, but he seemed so little to need sympathy that I experienced some shame at the recollection of what I had already hazarded. Besides, his reserve was again frozen over, and my frankness was congealed beneath it. Such being the case, I felt not a little surprised when he raised his head suddenly from his desk, and said, "You see, Jane, the battle is fought, the victory won."

I did not immediately reply; after a moment's hesitation I answered, "But are you sure you are not in the position of those conquerors whose triumphs have cost them too dear?"

"I think not; and if I were, it does not much signify. My way is now clear; I thank God for it!" So saying, he returned to his papers.

As our mutual happiness (i.e., Diana's, Mary's and mine) settled into a quieter character, St. John stayed more at home; he sat with us in the same room, sometimes for hours together. While Mary drew, Diana pursued a course of reading. I fagged away at German while St. John pondered some Eastern tongue, the acquisition of which he thought necessary to his plans.

One afternoon, Diana and Mary having gone to Morton, I stayed at home because I had a cold. I sat reading Schiller; St. John, deciphering his crabbed Oriental scrolls. I happened to look his way; there I found myself under the influence of the ever watchful blue eye.

"Jane, I want you to give up German, and learn Hindustani."

"You are not in earnest?"

"In such earnest that I must have it so, and I will tell you why."

He then went on to explain that Hindustani was the language he was studying; that, as he advanced, he was apt to forget the commencement; that it would assist him greatly to have a pupil with whom he might again and again go over the elements. Would I do him this favor?

St. John was not a man to be lightly refused: I consented. I found him a very patient master; and when I fulfilled his expectations, he, in his own way, fully testified his approbation. By degrees, he acquired a certain influence over me that took away my liberty of mind. I daily wished more to please him; but to do so, I felt daily more and more that I must disown half my nature, force myself to the adoption of pursuits for which I had no natural vocation.

Not his ascendancy, alone, however, held me in thrall as the winter wore on. It began to be easy enough for me to look sad: a cankering evil drained my happiness at its source—the evil of suspense.

Perhaps you think I had forgotten Mr. Rochester, reader, amidst these changes of place and fortune. Not for a moment. The craving to know what had become of him followed me everywhere. In the course of my necessary correspondence with Mr. Briggs about the will, I had inquired if he knew anything of Mr. Rochester's present residence and state of health; but he was quite ignorant of all concerning him. I then wrote to Mrs. Fairfax, entreating information on the subject. I was astonished when a fortnight passed without reply; but when two months wore away, and day after day the post arrived and brought nothing for me, I fell a prey to the keenest anxiety.

I wrote again: there was a chance of my first letter having missed; but when half a year wasted in vain expectancy my hope died out, and then I felt dark indeed.

Winter passed; a fine spring shone round me, but I could not enjoy it. One day I had come to my studies in lower spirits than usual. St. John called me to his side to read; in attempting to do this my voice failed me, words were lost in sobs. He and I were the only occupants of the parlor: Diana was practicing her music in the drawing room, Mary was gardening. My companion expressed no surprise at this emotion; he only said:

"We will wait a few minutes, Jane, till you are composed." And while I smothered the paroxysm with all haste, he sat calm and patient. I resumed my task, and succeeded in completing it. St. John put away my books and his, locked his desk, and said:

"Now, Jane, you shall take a walk, and with me. Put on your things."

"I will call Diana and Mary."

"No. I want only one companion this morning."

In ten minutes we were treading the wild track of the glen. The month was May, and the breeze came over the hills sweet with scents of heath and rush; the sky was of stainless blue; the stream descending the ravine caught golden gleams from the sun. As we left the track, we trod a soft turf, mossy fine and emerald green, minutely enameled with a tiny white flower. "Let us rest here," said St. John, as we reached a battalion of rocks guarding a sort of pass, beyond which the beck rushed down a waterfall. I took a seat, St. John stood near me. He looked up the pass; with his eye he bade farewell to something.

"And I shall see it again," he said aloud, "in dreams, when I sleep by the Ganges; and again, when another slumber overcomes me, on the shore of a darker stream."

Strange words of a strange love! He sat down; for half an hour we never spoke; that interval passed, he recommenced, "Jane, I go in six weeks; I have taken my berth in an East Indiaman which sails on the twentieth of June."

"God will protect you, for you have undertaken His work," I answered.

"Yes," said he, "there is my glory and joy. I am the servant of an infallible Master. It seems strange to me that all round me do not burn to enlist under the same banner."

"All have not your power, and it would be folly for the feeble to wish to march with the strong."

"I do not speak to the feeble, or think of them; I address only such as are worthy of the work, and, when found, it is right to stir them up—to speak Heaven's message in their ear."

"If they are really qualified for the task, will not their own hearts be the first to inform them of it?"

I felt as if an awful charm was gathering over me: I trembled to hear some fatal word spoken which would at once declare and rivet the spell.

"And what does *your* heart say?" demanded St. John.

"My heart is mute, my heart is mute," I answered, struck and thrilled.

"Then I must speak for it," continued the deep, relentless voice. "Jane, come with me to India; come as my helpmeet and fellow laborer."

The glen and sky spun round, the hills heaved!

"Oh, St. John!" I cried. "Have some mercy!"

I appealed to one who, in the discharge of what he believed his duty, knew neither mercy nor remorse. He continued, "God and nature intended you for a missionary's wife. You are formed for labor, not for love. A missionary's wife you must—shall be. You shall be mine. I claim you for my Sovereign's service."

"I am not fit for it; I have no vocation," I said.

He had calculated on these first objections; indeed, as he leaned back against the crag behind him, I saw he was prepared for a long and trying opposition.

"Humility, Jane," said he, "is the groundwork of Christian virtues: you say right that you are not fit for the work. Who is fit for it? Or who, that ever was truly called, believed himself worthy of the summons? Think like me, Jane—trust like me. It is the Rock of Ages I ask you to lean on; do not doubt but it will bear the weight of your human weakness."

"I do not understand a missionary life; I have never studied missionary labors."

"There I, humble as I am, can give you the aid you want; I can set your task from hour to hour, stand by you always. This I could do in the beginning. Soon (for I know your powers) you would be as strong and apt as myself. Jane, you are docile, diligent, courageous; cease to mistrust yourself. I can trust you unreservedly. As a conductress of Indian schools, and a helper amongst Indian women, your assistance will be to me invaluable."

My iron shroud contracted round me; persuasion advanced with slow sure step. I demanded a quarter of an hour to think, before I again hazarded a reply. "Very willingly," he rejoined, and rising, he strode a little distance up the pass, threw himself down on a swell of heath, and there lay still.

"I *can* do what he wants me to do," I meditated. "That is, if life be spared me. But I feel mine is not the existence to be long protracted under an Indian sun. What then? When my time came to die he would resign me, in all serenity, to the God who gave me. The case is very plain before me. In leaving England, I should leave a loved but empty land—Mr. Rochester is not there; and if he were, what is, what can that ever be to me? My business is to live without him now. Of course I must seek another interest in life to replace the one lost; is not the occupation St. John now offers me truly the most glorious man can adopt or God assign? Consent, then, to his demand is possible, but for one dreadful item. It is—that he asks me to be his wife, and has no more of a husband's heart for me than that frowning giant of a rock. He prizes me as a soldier would a good weapon, and that is all. Unmarried to him, this would never grieve me; but can I receive from him the bridal ring, endure all the forms of love (which I doubt not he would scrupulously observe) and know that the spirit was quite absent? No; such a martyrdom would be monstrous. As his sister, I might accompany him—not as his wife. I will tell him so."

I looked towards the knoll: his face turned to me. He started to his feet, and approached.

"I am ready to go to India, if I may go free. You have hitherto been my adopted brother, I, your adopted sister; let us continue as such. You and I had better not marry."

He shook his head. "Adopted fraternity will not do in this case. Either our union must be consecrated by marriage, or it cannot exist; practical obstacles oppose themselves to any other plan. Consider a moment, Jane—your sense will guide you."

My sense directed me only to the fact that we did not love each other as man and wife should, and therefore it inferred we ought not to marry. I said so. "St. John," I returned, "I regard you as a brother—you, me as a sister; so let us continue."

"We cannot," he answered, with sharp determination. "To fulfill the mission of your great Master I need you as a wife: the sole helpmeet I can influence efficiently in life, and retain absolutely till death."

I shuddered as he spoke: I felt his influence in my marrow.

"Seek one elsewhere than in me, St. John; seek one fitted to you."

"One fitted to my purpose, you mean—fitted to my vocation. Again I tell you it is not the insignificant private individual I wish to mate; it is a missionary."

"And I will give the missionary my energies—it is all he wants—but not myself; that would be only adding the husk and shell to the kernel."

"Do you think God will be satisfied with half an oblation? I cannot accept on His behalf a divided allegiance; it must be entire."

"Oh, I will give my heart to God," I said. "*You* do not want it."

I will not swear, reader, that there was not something of repressed sarcasm in the tone in which I uttered this sentence. I had silently feared St. John till now, because I had not understood him. How much of him was saint, how much mortal, I could not heretofore tell, but revelations were being made in this conference. I saw his fallibilities: I understood that, sitting there where I did, on the bank of heath, I sat at the feet of a man erring as I. The veil fell from his hardness and despotism. Having felt in him the presence of these qualities, I felt his imperfection, and I took courage.

He was silent after I had uttered the last sentence, and I presently risked an upward glance at his countenance. His eye, bent on me, expressed at once stern surprise and keen inquiry. Is she sarcastic, and sarcastic to *me!* it seemed to say.

"Do not let us forget that this is a solemn matter," he said ere long. "I trust, Jane, you are in earnest when you say you will give your heart to God; it is all I want. Once wrench your heart from man, and fix it on your Maker, the advancement of that Maker's spiritual kingdom on earth will be your chief delight and endeavor."

"I repeat: I freely consent to go with you as your fellow missionary, but not as your wife; I cannot marry you and become part of you."

"A part of me you must become," he answered steadily; "otherwise the whole bargain is void. How can I, a man not yet thirty, take out with me to India a girl of nineteen unless she be married to me? Jane, you would not repent marrying me; be certain of that. Undoubtedly enough of love would follow to render the union right even in your eyes."

"I scorn your idea of love," I could not help saying, as I rose up and stood before him, leaning my back against the rock. "I scorn the counterfeit sentiment you offer; yes, St. John, and I scorn you when you offer it."

He looked at me fixedly, compressing his well-cut lips while he did so. "I scarcely expected to hear that expression from you," he said: "I think I have done and uttered nothing to deserve scorn."

I was touched by his gentle tone, and overawed by his high, calm mien.

"Forgive me the words, St. John, but it is your own fault that I have been roused to speak so unguardedly. You have introduced a topic on which our natures are at variance: the very name of love is an apple of discord between us. My dear cousin, abandon your scheme of marriage—forget it."

"No," said he; "it is a long-cherished scheme, and the only one which can secure my great end, but I shall urge you no further at present. Tomorrow I leave home for Cambridge; I have many friends there to whom I should wish to say farewell. I shall be absent a fortnight—take that space of time to consider my offer; and do not forget, that if you reject it, it is not me you deny, but God."

As I walked by his side homeward, I read well in his iron silence all he felt towards me: the disappointment of an austere and despotic nature, which has met resistance where it expected submission—the disapprobation of a cool, inflexible judgment, which had detected in another feelings and views in which it has no power to sympathize. In short, as a man, he would have wished to coerce me into obedience; it was only as a sincere Christian he bore so patiently with my perversity.

HE DID NOT LEAVE FOR CAMBRIDGE the next day, as he had said he would. He deferred his departure a whole week; and during that time he made me feel what severe punishment a good yet implacable man can inflict on one who has offended him. Without one overt act of hostility, one upbraiding word, he contrived to impress me momently with the conviction that I was put beyond the pale of his favor.

He did not abstain from conversing with me: he even called me as usual each morning to join him at his desk; but he managed to extract from every deed and every phrase the spirit of interest and approval which had formerly communicated a certain austere charm to his language and manner. To me, he was in reality become no longer flesh, but marble.

The night before he left home, happening to see him walking in the garden about sunset, and remembering that this man, alienated as he now was, had once saved my life, and that we were near relations, I was moved to make a last attempt to regain his friendship. I went out and approached him as he stood leaning over the little gate; I spoke to the point at once.

"St. John, I am unhappy because you are still angry with me. Let us be friends."

"Are we not friends?" was the unmoved reply. "For my part, I wish you no ill and all good."

"When you go to India, will you leave me so, without a kinder word than you have yet spoken?"

He now turned and faced me. "When I go to India, Jane, will I leave you? What, do you not go to India?"

"You said I could not, unless I married you."

"And you will not marry me? You adhere to that resolution?"

Reader, do you know, as I do, what terror those cold people can put into the ice of their questions?

"No, St. John, I will not marry you. I adhere to my resolution."

"Once more, why this refusal?" he asked.

"Formerly," I answered, "because you did not love me; now because you almost hate me. If I were to marry you, you would kill me. You are killing me now."

His lips and cheeks turned white—quite white.

"*I should kill you—I am killing you?* Your words are such as ought not to be used: violent, unfeminine and untrue. They merit severe reproof. They would seem inexcusable; but that it is the duty of man to forgive his fellow, even until seventy-and-seven times."

I had finished the business now. While earnestly wishing to erase from his mind the trace of my former offense, I had stamped on that tenacious surface another and far deeper impression: I had burnt it in.

"Now, you will indeed hate me," I said. "I see I have made an eternal enemy of you."

A fresh wrong did these words inflict; the worse, because they touched on the truth. That bloodless lip quivered to a temporary spasm. I was heart-wrung.

"You utterly misinterpret my words," I said, seizing his hand. "I have no intention to pain you—indeed, I have not."

Most bitterly he smiled—most decidedly he withdrew his hand from mine. "And now you recall your promise, and will not go to India at all, I presume?" said he, after a considerable pause.

"Yes, I will, as your curate, if you like, but never as your wife."

Again he turned pale; but, as before, controlled his passion perfectly. He answered emphatically, but calmly, "A female curate, who is not my wife, would never suit me. With me, then, it seems, you cannot go; but if you are sincere in your offer, I will speak to a married missionary, whose wife needs a coadjutor. Thus you may still be spared the dishonor of breaking your promise."

Now I never had, as the reader knows, either given any formal promise, or entered into any engagement. I replied, "There is no dishonor, no breach of promise. I am not under the slightest obligation to go to India, especially with strangers. With you I would have ventured much; because I admire, confide in, and, as a sister, I love you. But I am convinced that, go when and with whom I would, I should not live long in that climate."

"Ah, you are afraid of yourself," he said, curling his lip.

"I am. God did not give me my life to throw away. Moreover, before I definitely resolve on quitting England, I will know for certain whether I cannot be of greater use by remaining in it than by leaving it."

"What do you mean?"

"It would be fruitless to attempt to explain, but there is a point on which I have long endured painful doubt; and I can go nowhere till by some means that doubt is removed."

"I know where your heart turns, and to what it clings. The interest you cherish is lawless and unconsecrated. You think of Mr. Rochester?" It was true. I confessed it by silence. "Are you going to seek Mr. Rochester?"

"I must find out what has become of him."

"It remains for me, then," he said, "to remember you in my prayers, and to entreat God for you, in all earnestness, that you may not indeed become a castaway."

He opened the gate, passed through it, and strayed away down the glen. He was soon out of sight.

On re-entering the parlor, I found Diana standing at the window, looking thoughtful. "Jane," she said, "you are always agitated and pale now. I am sure there is something the matter. Tell me what business St. John and you have on hand. St. John is a strange being—" She paused—I did not speak. She resumed, "That brother of mine cherishes peculiar views of some sort respecting you, I am sure. I wish he loved you—does he, Jane?"

I put her cool hand to my hot forehead. "No, Diana, not one whit."

"Mary and I had both concluded he wished you to marry him."

"He does—he has asked me to be his wife."

Diana clapped her hands. "That is what we hoped! You will marry him, Jane, won't you? And then he will stay in England."

"Far from that, Diana; his sole idea in proposing to me is to procure a fitting fellow laborer in his Indian toils."

"What?" she exclaimed. "Madness! You would not live three months there. You have not consented—have you, Jane?"

"I have refused to marry him—"

"And have consequently displeased him?" she suggested.

"Deeply. He will never forgive me, I fear; yet I offered to accompany him as his sister."

"You do not love him then, Jane?"

"Not as a husband. We should never suit."

I was forced to meet St. John again at supper. During that meal he appeared as composed as usual. I had thought he would hardly speak to me, and I was certain he had given up the pursuit of his matrimonial scheme; the sequel showed I was mistaken on both points. He addressed me precisely in his ordinary manner, or what had, of late, been his ordinary manner—one scrupulously polite. No doubt he had invoked the help of the Holy Spirit to subdue the anger I had roused in him, and now believed he had forgiven me once more.

After evening prayers in the parlor, we took leave of him; he was to go at a very early hour in the morning. Diana and Mary, having kissed him good night, left the room—in compliance, I think, with a whispered hint from him. I tendered my hand, and wished him a pleasant journey.

"Thank you, Jane. As I said, I shall return from Cambridge in a fortnight; that space, then, is yet left you for reflection. If I listened to human pride, I should say no more to you of marriage with me; but I listen to my duty, and keep steadily in view my first aim—to do all things to the glory of God."

He had spoken earnestly, mildly: his look was not, indeed, that of a lover beholding his mistress; but it was that of a pastor recalling his wandering sheep. I felt veneration for St. John—veneration so strong that I was tempted to cease struggling with him—to rush down the torrent of his will into the gulf of his existence, and there lose my own. I was almost as hard beset by him now as I had been once before, in a different way, by another.

"Could you decide now?" asked the missionary. The inquiry was put in gentle tones; he drew me to him gently. Oh, that gentleness! How far more potent is it than force! Yet I knew all the time, if I yielded now, I should not the less be made to repent, someday, of my former rebellion.

"I could decide if I were but certain," I answered; "were I but convinced that it is God's will I should marry you, I could vow to marry you here and now—come afterwards what would!"

"My prayers are heard!" ejaculated St. John. He pressed his hand firmer on my head, as if he claimed me; he surrounded me with his arm, almost as if he loved me; I contended with my inward dimness of vision, before which clouds yet rolled. I sincerely, deeply, fervently longed to do what was right; and only that. "Show me, show me the path!" I entreated of Heaven. I was excited more than I had ever been; and whether what followed was the effect of excitement, the reader shall judge.

All the house was still; for I believe all, except St. John and me, were now retired. The one candle was dying out; the room was full of moonlight which shone in through the uncurtained window. My heart beat fast and thick; I heard its throb. Suddenly it stood still to an inexpressible feeling that thrilled it through, and passed at once to my head and extremities. The feeling was not like an electric shock, but it was quite as sharp, as strange, as startling: it acted on my senses as if their utmost activity hitherto had been but torpor; eye and ear waited, while the flesh quivered on my bones.

"What have you heard? What do you see?" asked St. John. I saw nothing: but I heard a voice somewhere cry:

"Jane! Jane! Jane!" Nothing more.

"Oh God! What is it?" I gasped.

I might have said, "Where is it?" for it did not seem in the room—nor in the house—nor in the garden. It did not come out of the air—nor from under the earth—nor from overhead. I had heard it—where, or whence, forever impossible to know! And it was a known, loved, well-remembered voice—that of Edward Rochester; and it spoke in pain and woe, wildly, eerily, urgently.

"I am coming!" I cried. "Wait for me! Oh, I will come!" I flew to the door, and looked into the passage: it was dark. I ran out into the garden: it was void.

"Where are you?" I exclaimed.

The hills beyond Marsh Glen sent the answer faintly back: "Where are you?" I listened. The wind sighed low in the firs; all was moorland loneliness and midnight hush.

I broke from St. John, who had followed and would have detained me. It was *my* time to assume ascendancy. I told him I desired him to leave me: I must, and would be, alone. He obeyed at once. Where there is energy to command well enough, obedience never fails. I mounted to my chamber; locked myself in; fell on my knees and prayed in my way—a different way to St. John's, but effective in its own fashion. I seemed to penetrate very near a Mighty Spirit, and my soul rushed out in gratitude at His feet. I rose from the thanksgiving—took a resolve—and lay down, unscared, enlightened—eager but for the daylight.

CHAPTER XIX

THE DAYLIGHT CAME. I ROSE AT DAWN, and for an hour or two arranged my things in my chamber in the order wherein I should wish to leave them during a brief absence. Meantime, I heard St. John quit his room and stop at my door. A slip of paper was passed under it. It bore these words:

> You left me too suddenly last night. Had you stayed but a little longer, you would have laid your hand on the Christian's cross and the angel's crown. I shall expect your clear decision when I return this day fortnight. I shall pray for you hourly.
>
> Yours,
> St. John

It was the first of June, yet the morning was chilly; rain beat on my casement. Looking out the window, I saw St. John traverse the garden and take his way over the misty moors in the direction of Whitcross—there he would meet the coach.

In a few more hours I shall succeed you in that track, cousin, thought I; I too have some to see and ask after in England, before I depart forever.

At breakfast I announced to Diana and Mary that I was going on a journey, and should be absent at least four days.

"Alone, Jane?" they asked.

Yes; it was to see, or hear news of, a friend about whom I had for some time been uneasy.

With their true natural delicacy, they abstained from comment, except that Diana asked me if I was sure I was well enough to travel. I looked pale, she observed. I replied that nothing ailed me save anxiety of mind, which I hoped soon to alleviate.

Soon after four o'clock, I stood at the foot of the signpost of Whitcross, waiting the arrival of the coach. Amidst the silence of those solitary roads and deserted hills, I heard it approach from a great distance. It stopped as I beckoned. I entered—once more on the road to Thornfield, I felt like the messenger pigeon flying home.

It was a journey of six-and-thirty hours. I had set out from Whitcross on a Tuesday afternoon, and early on Thursday morning the coach stopped to water the horses at a wayside inn, situated in the midst of scenery whose green hedges and low pastoral hills met my eye like the lineaments of a familiar face.

"How far is Thornfield Hall from here?" I asked of the ostler.

"Two miles, ma'am, across the fields."

My journey is closed, I thought to myself. I got out of the coach, gave a box I had into the ostler's charge, to be kept till I called for it, paid my fare, and was going. The brightening day gleamed on the sign of the inn, and I read in gilt letters: THE ROCHESTER ARMS. My heart leapt up: I was already on my master's very lands. It fell again; the thought struck it:

"Your master himself may be beyond the British Channel for

aught you know; and then, if he is at Thornfield Hall, who besides him is there? His lunatic wife, and you dare not speak to him or seek his presence. You had better go no farther," urged the monitor. "Ask information of the people at the inn; inquire if Mr. Rochester be at home."

The suggestion was sensible, and yet I could not force myself to act on it. I so dreaded a reply that would crush me with despair. There was the stile before me—the very fields through which I had hurried, blind, deaf, distracted, on the morning I fled from Thornfield; ere I well knew what course I had resolved to take, I was in the midst of them. How fast I walked! How I looked forward to catch the first view of the well-known woods! With what feelings I welcomed trees I knew, and familiar glimpses of meadow and hill!

At last the woods rose; the rookery clustered dark; a loud cawing broke the morning stillness. Another field crossed—and there were the courtyard walls—the house itself was still hidden by the rookery. My first view of it shall be in front, I determined, where its bold battlements will strike the eye nobly at once, and where I can single out my master's very window; perhaps he will be standing at it—he rises early.

I had coasted along the lower wall of the orchard—turned its angle; there was a gate just there, between two stone pillars, crowned by stone balls. From behind one pillar, I could peep round quietly at the full front of the mansion.

The crows sailing overhead perhaps watched me while I took this survey. I wonder what they thought. They must have considered I was very careful and timid at first, and that gradually I grew very bold and reckless. A peep, and then a long stare; a sudden stop full in front of the great mansion, and a protracted, hardy gaze towards it.

I looked with timorous joy towards a stately house; I saw a blackened ruin.

No need to cower behind a gatepost, indeed! No need to listen for doors opening—to fancy steps on the pavement or the gravel! The lawn, the grounds were trodden and waste; the portal yawned wide. The front was, as I had once seen it in a dream, but a shell-like wall, perforated with paneless windows; no roof, no chimneys—all had crashed in.

And there was the silence of death about it: the solitude of a lonesome wild. No wonder that letters addressed to people here had never received an answer. The grim blackness of the stones

told by what fate the Hall had fallen—by conflagration. But how kindled? What story belonged to this disaster? What loss, besides mortar and woodwork, had followed upon it?

Some answer must be had to these questions. I could find it no-where but at the inn, and thither I returned. The host himself brought my breakfast into the parlor. I requested him to sit down—I had some questions to ask him. But when he complied, I scarcely knew how to begin, such horror had I of the possible answers.

"You know Thornfield Hall, of course?" I managed to say at last.

"Yes, ma'am; I lived there once. I was the late Mr. Rochester's butler."

The late! I seemed to have received with full force the blow I had been trying to evade.

"The late!" I gasped. "Is he dead?"

"I mean the present gentleman, Mr. Edward's, father," he explained. I breathed again; fully assured by these words that Mr. Edward—*my* Mr. Rochester (God bless him, wherever he was!) was at least alive. Gladdening words! It seemed I could hear all that was to come—whatever the disclosures might be—with comparative tranquillity.

"Is Mr. Rochester living at Thornfield now?" I asked, knowing, of course, what the answer would be.

"No, ma'am—oh, no! I suppose you are a stranger in these parts, or you would have heard what happened last autumn. Thornfield Hall is quite a ruin: it was burnt down just about harvest time. A dreadful calamity! The fire broke out at dead of night, and before the engines arrived from Millcote, the building was one mass of flame. It was a terrible spectacle; I witnessed it myself."

"At dead of night!" I muttered. Yes, that was ever the hour of fatality at Thornfield. "Was it known how it originated?"

"They guessed, ma'am, they guessed. You are not perhaps aware," he continued, edging his chair a little nearer the table, and speaking low, "that there was a lady—a—a lunatic, kept in the house?"

"I have heard something of it."

"She was kept in close confinement, ma'am; people for years was not absolutely certain of her existence. They said Mr. Edward had brought her from abroad, and some believed she had been his mistress. But a queer thing happened a year since—a very queer thing."

I feared now to hear my own story. I endeavored to recall him to the main fact.

"And this lady?"

"This lady, ma'am," he answered, "turned out to be Mr. Rochester's wife! The discovery was brought about in the strangest way. There was a young lady, a governess at the Hall, that Mr. Rochester fell in—"

"But the fire," I suggested.

"I'm coming to that, ma'am—that Mr. Edward fell in love with. The servants say they never saw anybody so much in love as he was, he was after her continually. She was a little small thing, they say, almost like a child; I've heard Leah, the housemaid, tell of her. Mr. Rochester was about forty, and this governess not twenty. Well, he would marry her."

"You shall tell me this part of the story another time," I said, "but now I have a particular reason for wishing to hear all about the fire. Was it suspected that this lunatic, Mrs. Rochester, had any hand in it?"

"You've hit it, ma'am; it's quite certain that it was her that set it going. She had a woman to take care of her called Mrs. Poole, an able woman in her line, and very trustworthy, but for one fault: she kept a private bottle of gin by her, and now and then took a drop overmuch. It was dangerous; for when Mrs. Poole was fast asleep, after the gin, the mad lady, who was as cunning as a witch, would take the keys out of her pocket, let herself out of her chamber, and go roaming about the house, doing any mischief that came into her head.

"On this night, she set fire first to the hangings of the room next to her own, and then she made her way to the chamber that had been the governess's and she kindled the bed there; but there was nobody sleeping in it, fortunately. The governess had run away two months before; and for all Mr. Rochester sought her as if she had been the most precious thing he had in the world, he never could hear a word of her, and he grew quite savage on his disappointment. He would be alone, too. He sent Mrs. Fairfax, the housekeeper, away to her friends at a distance; Miss Adèle, a ward he had, was put to school. He broke off acquaintance with all the gentry, and shut himself up like a hermit at the Hall."

"What! Did he not leave England?"

"Leave England? Bless you, no! He would not cross the door-stones of the house, except at night, when he walked just like a ghost about the grounds and in the orchard as if he had lost his senses—which it is my opinion he had; for a more spirited, bolder, keener gentleman than he was before that midge of a governess crossed him, you never saw, ma'am. I knew him from a boy, you see; and for my part I have often wished that Miss Eyre had been sunk in the sea before she came to Thornfield Hall."

"Then Mr. Rochester was at home when the fire broke out?"

"Yes, indeed was he; and he went up to the attic when all was burning, and helped the servants down himself—and went back to get his mad wife. And then they called out to him that she was on the roof. She was standing above the battlements, and shouting out till they could hear her a mile off; I saw her with my own eyes. She was a big woman, and had long, black hair; we could see it streaming against the flames as she stood. We witnessed Mr. Rochester ascend through the skylight onto the roof, we heard him call 'Bertha!' We saw him approach her; and then, ma'am, she yelled and gave a spring, and the next minute she lay smashed on the pavement, dead as the stones on which her brains and blood were scattered."

"Good God!"

"You may well say so, ma'am: it was frightful!" He shuddered.

"And afterwards?" I urged.

"Well, ma'am, afterwards the house was burned to the ground."

"Were any other lives lost?"

"No—perhaps it would have been better if there had."

"What do you mean?"

"Poor Mr. Edward!" he ejaculated. "I little thought ever to have seen it! Some say it was a just judgment on him for wanting to take another wife while he had one living, but I pity him, for my part."

"You said he was alive?" I exclaimed.

"Yes, yes, he is alive; but many think he had better be dead."

"Why? How?" My blood was again running cold.

"He is stone-blind," the man said at last.

I had dreaded worse. I had dreaded he was mad. I summoned strength to ask what had caused this calamity.

"It was all his own courage, and his kindness, in a way, ma'am; he wouldn't leave the house till everyone else was out before him. As he came down the great staircase at last, after Mrs. Rochester had flung herself from the battlements, there was a great crash—all fell. He was taken out from under the ruins, alive, but sadly hurt; one eye was knocked out, and one hand so crushed that the surgeon had to amputate it. The other eye inflamed; he lost the sight of that also. He is now helpless, indeed—blind and a cripple."

"Where is he? Where does he now live?"

"At Ferndean, a manor house on a farm he has, about thirty miles off. Quite a desolate spot."

"Who is with him?"

"Old John and his wife. He is quite broken down, they say."

"Have you any sort of conveyance?"

"We have a chaise, ma'am."

"Let it be got ready instantly; and if your post boy can drive me to Ferndean before dark this day, I'll pay both you and him twice the hire you usually demand."

THE MANOR HOUSE OF FERNDEAN was a building of considerable antiquity and moderate size, deep buried in a wood. Mr. Rochester had often spoken of it. His father had purchased the estate for the sake of the game covers. He would have let the house, but could find no tenant, in consequence of its insalubrious site. Ferndean then remained uninhabited and unfurnished, with the exception of two or three rooms fitted up for the accommodation of the squire when he went there in the season to shoot.

To this house I came, just ere dark, on an evening marked by sad sky, cold gale and penetrating rain. The last mile I performed on foot, having dismissed the chaise and driver. Even when within a very short distance of the manor house, you could see nothing of it, so thick and dark grew the gloomy wood about it. Iron gates between granite pillars showed me where to enter, and passing through them, I found myself at once in the twilight of close-ranked trees.

I proceeded. At last my way opened, the trees thinned a little; presently I beheld the house—scarce, by this dim light, distinguishable from the trees, so dank and green were its decaying walls. There were no flowers, no garden beds around it; only a broad gravel walk girdling a grassplot, and this set in the heavy frame of the forest. It was as still as a church on a weekday; the pattering rain on the forest leaves was the only sound audible.

"Can there be life here?" I asked.

Yes, life of some kind there was, for I heard a movement—that narrow front door was unclosing, and some shape was about to issue from the grange.

It opened slowly; a figure came out into the twilight and stood on the step; a man without a hat; he stretched forth his hand as if to feel whether it rained. Dusk as it was, I had recognized him—it was my master, Edward Fairfax Rochester, and no other.

I stayed my step, almost my breath, and stood to watch him—myself unseen, and alas! to him invisible. His form was of the same strong contour as ever; his bearing was still erect, his hair was still raven-black. But in his countenance I saw a change that looked desperate and brooding. The caged eagle, whose gold-ringed eyes cruelty has extinguished, might look as looked that sightless Samson.

He descended the one step, and advanced slowly and gropingly towards the grassplot. Where was his daring stride now? Then he paused, as if he knew not which way to turn. He lifted his hand and opened his eyelids; gazed with a straining effort on the sky, and towards the amphitheater of trees. He stretched his right hand (the mutilated left arm he kept hidden in his bosom); he seemed to wish by touch to gain an idea of what lay around him; he relinquished the endeavor, folded his arms, and stood quiet and mute in the rain. At this moment John approached him from some quarter.

"Will you take my arm, sir?" he said. "There is a shower coming on; had you not better go in?"

"Let me alone," was the answer.

John withdrew, without having observed me. Mr. Rochester now tried to walk about: vainly—all was too uncertain. He groped his way back to the house, and, re-entering it, closed the door.

I now drew near and knocked; John's wife opened for me. "Mary," I said, "how are you?"

She started as if she had seen a ghost. I calmed her. To her hurried "Is it really you, Miss, come at this late hour to this 'only place?" I answered by taking her hand; and then I followed her into the kitchen, where John sat by a good fire. I explained to them that I had heard all which had happened since I left Thornfield, and that I was come to see Mr. Rochester. I asked John to go down to the turnpike house, where I had dismissed the chaise, and bring my trunk, and then, while I removed my bonnet, I arranged with Mary to be accommodated at the manor house for the night. Just at this moment the parlor bell rang.

"When you go in," said I, "tell your master that a person wishes to speak to him, but do not give my name."

"I don't think he will see you," she answered; "he refuses everybody."

When she returned, I inquired what he had said.

"You are to send in your name and your business," she replied. She then proceeded to fill a glass with water, and place it on a tray, together with candles.

"Is that what he rang for?" I asked.

"Yes. He always has candles brought in at dark, though he is blind."

"Give the tray to me, I will carry it in."

I took it from her hand; she pointed me out the parlor door. The tray shook as I held it; the water spilled from the glass; my heart struck my ribs loud and fast. Mary opened the door for me, and shut it behind me.

This parlor looked gloomy: a neglected handful of fire burned low in the grate; and, leaning over it, with his head supported against the mantelpiece, appeared the blind tenant of the room. His old dog, Pilot, lay on one side, coiled up as if afraid of being inadvertently trodden upon. Pilot pricked up his ears when I came in; then he jumped up with a yelp and a whine, and bounded towards me. I set the tray on the table; then patted him, and said softly, "Lie down!" Mr. Rochester turned mechanically to *see* what the commotion was, but as he *saw* nothing, he returned and sighed.

"Give me the water, Mary," he said.

I approached him with the glass. Pilot followed me, still excited.

"What is the matter?" he inquired.

"Down, Pilot!" I again said. He checked the water on its way to his lips, and seemed to listen; he drank, and put the glass down. "This is you, Mary, is it not?"

"Mary is in the kitchen," I answered.

He put out his hand with a quick gesture, but not seeing where I stood, he did not touch me. "Who is this? Who is this?" he demanded. "Answer me—speak again!"

"Will you have a little more water, sir?"

"*Who* is it? *What* is it? Who speaks?"

"Pilot knows me, and John and Mary know I am here. I came only this evening," I answered.

"Great God! What delusion has come over me? What sweet madness has seized me?"

"No delusion—no madness; your mind, sir, is too strong for delusion, your health too sound for frenzy."

"And where is the speaker? Oh! I *cannot* see, but I must feel, or my heart will stop!"

He groped; I arrested his wandering hand, and prisoned it in both mine.

"Her very fingers!" he cried. "Her small, slight fingers! If so, there must be more of her."

The muscular hand broke from my custody; my arm was seized, my shoulder—neck—waist—I was entwined and gathered to him.

"Is it Jane? *What* is it? This is her shape—this is her size—"

"And this her voice," I added. "She is all here; her heart, too. God bless you, sir! I am glad to be so near you again."

"Jane Eyre! Jane Eyre!" was all he said.

"My dear master," I answered, "I have found you out—I am come back to you."

"My living darling! These are certainly her limbs, and these her features; but I cannot be so blest, after all my misery. It is a dream; such dreams as I have had at night when I have clasped her once more to my heart, and kissed her, and felt that she loved me, and trusted that she would not leave me."

"Which I never will, sir, from this day."

"Never will, says the vision? But I always woke and found it an empty mockery; and I was desolate and abandoned—my life dark, lonely, hopeless. Gentle, soft dream, nestling in my arms now, you will fly, too, as your sisters have all fled—"

"There, sir—and there!"

I pressed my lips to his—I swept his hair from his brow and kissed that too. He suddenly seemed to rouse himself. The conviction of the reality of all this seized him. "It is you, Jane? You are come back to me, then?"

"I am."

"And you do not lie dead in some ditch under some stream? And you are not a pining outcast amongst strangers?"

"No, sir; I am an independent woman now. My uncle in Madeira is dead, and he left me five thousand pounds."

"Ah, this is practical—this is real!" he cried. "I should never dream that. What, Janet! Are you a rich woman?"

"Quite rich, sir. If you won't let me live with you, I can build a house of my own close up to your door, and you may come and sit in my parlor when you want company."

"But as you are rich, Jane, you have now, no doubt, friends who will look after you, and not suffer you to devote yourself to a blind cripple like me?"

"I told you I am independent, sir, as well as rich. I am my own mistress."

"And you will stay with me?"

"Certainly—unless you object, I will be your neighbor, your nurse, your housekeeper. Cease to look so melancholy, my dear master; you shall not be left desolate, so long as I live."

He replied not; he seemed abstracted; he half opened his lips as if to speak; he closed them again. I felt a little embarrassed. Perhaps I had too rashly overleaped conventionalities; I had indeed made my proposal from the idea that he would ask me to be his wife. But his countenance becoming overcast, I suddenly remembered that I might have been all wrong, and was perhaps playing the fool unwittingly; and I began gently to withdraw myself from his arms—but he eagerly snatched me closer.

"No—no—Jane; you must not go. No—I have touched you, heard you. I cannot give up these joys. I have little left in myself—I must have you."

"Well, sir, I will stay with you."

"Yes—but you understand one thing by staying with me, and I understand another. You, perhaps, could make up your mind to wait on me as a kind little nurse, and that ought to suffice for me, no doubt. I suppose I should now entertain none but fatherly feelings for you; do you think so? Come—tell me."

"I will think what you like, sir. I am content to be only your nurse, if you think it better."

"But you cannot always be my nurse, Janet; you are young—you must marry one day."

"I don't care about being married."

"You should care, Janet. If I were what I once was, I would try to make you care—but—a sightless block!"

He relapsed again into gloom. I, on the contrary, took fresh courage: these last words gave me an insight as to where the difficulty lay; and as it was no difficulty with me, I felt relieved from my previous embarrassment. I resumed a livelier vein of conversation.

"It is time someone undertook to rehumanize you," said I, parting his thick and long uncut locks, "for I see you are being metamorphosed into a lion, or something of that sort. Your hair reminds me of eagles' feathers. But now, let me leave you an instant, to make a better fire, and have the hearth swept up. Can you tell when there is a good fire?"

"Yes; with the right eye I see a glow—a ruddy haze."

"Can you see me?"

"No, my fairy, but I am only too thankful to hear and feel you."

"When do you take supper?"

"I never take supper."

"But you shall have some tonight. I am hungry; so are you, I daresay, only you forget."

Summoning Mary, I soon had the room in more cheerful order. I prepared him, likewise, a comfortable repast. With pleasure and ease I talked to him during supper, and for a long time after; all I said or did seemed either to console or revive him. Blind as he was, smiles played over his face, joy dawned on his forehead: his lineaments softened and warmed.

After supper, he began to ask me many questions, but I gave him only very partial replies: it was too late to enter into particulars that night. Besides, I wished to touch no deep-thrilling chord: my sole present aim was to cheer him. Cheered he was, and yet but by fits. If a moment's silence broke the conversation, he would turn restless, touch me, then say, "Jane."

"You are altogether a human being, Jane? You are certain of that?"

"I conscientiously believe so, Mr. Rochester."

"There is enchantment in the very hour I am now spending with you. How can it be that Jane is with me, and says she loves me? Will she not depart as suddenly as she came? Tomorrow I fear I shall find her no more."

A commonplace, practical reply was, I was sure, the most reassuring for him in this frame of mind.

"Have you a pocket comb about you, sir?" I asked.

"What for, Jane?"

"Just to comb out this shaggy black mane. I find you rather alarming, when I examine you close at hand."

"Humph! The wickedness has not been taken out of you, wherever you have sojourned."

"Yet I have been with good people—quite refined and exalted."

"Who the deuce have you been with, Jane?"

"You shall not get it out of me tonight, sir; you must wait

till tomorrow; to leave my tale half told, will, you know, be a sort of security that I shall appear at your breakfast table to finish it. Now I'll leave you; I've been traveling these last three days, and I am tired. Good night."

"Just one word, Jane: were there only ladies in the house where you have been?"

I laughed and made my escape, still laughing as I ran upstairs.

Very early the next morning I heard him up and astir, wandering from one room to another. As soon as Mary came down I heard the question: "Is Miss Eyre here?" Then: "Which room did you put her into? Was it dry? Is she up? Go and ask if she wants anything, and when she will come down."

I came down as soon as I thought there was a prospect of breakfast. Entering the room softly, I had a view of him before he discovered my presence. He sat in his chair—still, but not at rest—expectant evidently; the lines of now habitual sadness marking his strong features. I had meant to be gay, but the powerlessness of the strong man touched my heart to the quick. Still I accosted him with what vivacity I could:

"It is a bright, sunny morning, sir," I said. "You shall have a walk soon."

I had wakened the glow; his features beamed.

"Oh, you are indeed there, my skylark! Come to me. You are not gone, not vanished? I heard one of your kind an hour ago, singing high over the wood, but its song had no music for me. To my ear all the melody on earth is concentrated in my Jane's tongue."

The water stood in my eyes to hear this avowal of his dependence: just as if a royal eagle, chained to a perch, should be forced to entreat a sparrow to become its purveyor. But I dashed off the salt drops, and busied myself with preparing breakfast.

Most of the morning was spent in the open air. I led him out of the wet and wild wood into some cheerful fields; I described to him how brilliantly green they were, how sparklingly blue was the sky. I sought a seat for him on a stump of a tree, nor did I refuse to let him, when seated, place me on his knee. Pilot lay beside us; all was quiet. He broke out suddenly while clasping me in his arms:

"Cruel, cruel deserter! Oh, Jane, what did I feel when I discovered you had fled from Thornfield, and when I could nowhere find you; and, after examining your apartment, ascertained that you had taken no money. What could my darling do, I asked, left destitute and penniless? And what did she do? Let me hear now."

Thus urged, I began the narrative of my experience for the last year. Of course, St. John Rivers' name came in frequently in the progress of my tale. When I had done, that name was immediately taken up.

"This St. John, then, is your cousin?"

"Yes."

"You have spoken of him often. Did you like him?"

"He was a good man, sir; I could not help liking him. He is untiringly active. Great and exalted deeds are what he lives to perform."

"Is he an able man, then?"

"Truly able."

"And his appearance?"

"He is handsome: tall, fair with blue eyes, and a Grecian profile."

(*Aside.*) "Damn him!" (*To me.*) "Did you like him, Jane?"

"Yes, Mr. Rochester, I liked him; but you asked me that before."

I perceived, of course, that jealousy had got hold of him. She stung him, but the sting gave him respite from the gnawing fang of melancholy. I would not, therefore, immediately charm the snake.

"Perhaps you would rather not sit any longer on my knee, Miss Eyre?" was the next somewhat unexpected observation.

"Why not, Mr. Rochester?"

"The picture you have just drawn is suggestive of a rather too overwhelming contrast. Your words have delineated very prettily a graceful Apollo; your eyes dwell on a Vulcan—a real blacksmith, and blind and lame into the bargain."

"I never thought of it before; but you certainly are rather like Vulcan, sir."

"Well, you can leave me, ma'am; but before you go"— and he retained me by a firmer grasp than ever —"you will be pleased just to answer me a question or two." He paused, and then followed this cross-examination. "How long did you reside with St. John and his sisters after your cousinship was discovered?"

"Five months."

"Did Rivers spend much time with the ladies of his family?"

"Yes; the back parlor was both his study and ours; he sat near the window, and we by the table."

"And what did you do?"

"I learned German at first."

"Did he teach you?"

"He did not understand German."

"Did he teach you nothing?"

"A little Hindustani."

"Of what use could Hindustani be to you?"

"He intended me to go with him to India."

"Ah, here I reach the root of the matter. He wanted you to marry him?"

"He asked me to marry him."

"Miss Eyre, I repeat it, you can leave me. Why do you remain perched on my knee, when I have given you notice to quit?"

"Because I am comfortable there."

"No, Jane, you are not comfortable there, because your heart is with this cousin—this St. John. Oh, till this moment, I thought my little Jane was all mine! But I am not a fool—go—"

"Where must I go, sir?"

"Your own way—with the husband you have chosen—this St. John Rivers."

"He is not my husband, nor ever will be. He does not love me; I do not love him. He wanted to marry me only because he thought I should make a suitable missionary's wife. He is good and great, but severe; and for me, cold as an iceberg."

I shuddered involuntarily, and clung instinctively closer to my blind but beloved master. He smiled.

"What, Jane! Is this true?"

"Absolutely, sir. Oh, you need not be jealous! I wanted to tease you a little to make you less sad. But could you but see how much I *do* love you, you would be proud and content. All my heart is yours, sir."

Again, as he kissed me, painful thoughts darkened his aspect.

"My seared vision! My crippled strength!" he murmured regretfully.

I caressed, in order to soothe him. I knew of what he was thinking, and wanted to speak for him, but dared not. As he turned aside his face a minute, I saw a tear slide from under the sealed eyelid. My heart swelled.

"I am no better than the old lightning-struck chestnut tree in Thornfield orchard," he remarked ere long. "And what right would that ruin have to bid a budding woodbine cover its decay with freshness?"

"You are no ruin, sir—no lightning-struck tree; you are green and vigorous. Plants will grow about your roots because they take delight in your shadow; and as they grow they will lean towards you because your strength offers them so safe a prop."

Again he smiled; I gave him comfort.

"You speak of friends, Jane?" he asked.

"Yes, of friends," I answered, rather hesitatingly, for I knew I meant more than friends, but could not tell what other word to employ. He helped me!

"Ah, Jane! But I want a wife."

"Do you, sir?"

"Yes; is it news to you?"

"Of course. You said nothing about it before."

"Is it unwelcome news?"

"That depends, sir—on your choice."

"Which you shall make for me, Jane. I will abide by your decision."

"Choose then, sir—*her who loves you best*."

"I will at least choose—*her I love best*. Jane, will you marry me?"

"Yes, sir."

"A blind and crippled man, twenty years older than you, whom you will have to wait on?"

"Yes, sir."

"Truly, Jane?"

"Most truly, sir."

"Oh, my darling! God bless you and reward you!"

"Mr. Rochester, I am rewarded now. To be your wife is, for me, to be as happy as I can be on earth."

"Then we have nothing in the world to wait for; we must be married instantly." He looked and spoke with eagerness; his old impetuosity was rising. "The third day from this must be our wedding day, Jane. Never mind fine clothes and jewels, now; all that is not worth a fillip."

"Mr. Rochester, I have just discovered the sun is far declined from its meridian, and Pilot is actually gone home to his dinner. Let me look at your watch."

He pursued his own thoughts without heeding me.

"Jane, you think me, I daresay, an irreligious dog, but my heart swells just now with gratitude to God. He judges not as man judges, but far more wisely. I did wrong: I would have sullied my innocent flower—the Omnipotent snatched it from me. Divine justice pursued its course; disasters came thick on me. You know I was proud of my strength; but what is it now, when I must give it over to foreign guidance? Of late, Jane, I began to see and acknowledge the hand of God in my doom. I began to experience remorse, repentance; I began sometimes to pray. Very brief prayers they were, but very sincere.

"Some days since—nay, I can number them, four—it was last Monday night, a singular mood came over me, one in which grief replaced frenzy. I had long had the impression that since I could nowhere find you, you must be dead. Late that night—perhaps it might be between eleven and twelve o'clock—ere I retired to my dreary rest, I supplicated God, that, if it seemed good to Him, I might soon be taken from this life, and admitted to that world to come, where there was still hope of rejoining Jane. I was in my own room, and sitting by the window, which was open: it soothed me to feel the balmy night air, though I could see no stars. I longed for thee, Janet! I asked of God, at once in anguish and humility, if I had not been long enough desolate, tormented; I asked if I might not soon taste bliss and peace once more; and the beginning and end of my heart's wishes broke involuntarily from my lips in the words—'Jane! Jane! Jane!'"

"Did you speak these words aloud?"

"I did, Jane. If any listener had heard me, he would have thought me mad, I pronounced them with such frantic energy."

"And it was last Monday night, somewhere near midnight?"

"Yes; but the time is of no consequence; what followed is the point. You will think me superstitious; nevertheless, this is true. As I exclaimed 'Jane! Jane! Jane!' a voice—I cannot tell whence the voice came, but I know whose voice it was—replied, 'I am coming! Wait for me!' And a moment after, went whispering on the wind, the words 'Where are you?'

"I'll tell you, if I can, the idea, the picture these words opened to my mind; yet it is difficult to express what I want to express. I could have deemed that in some wild, lone scene, Jane and I were meeting. In spirit, I believe we must have met. You no doubt were, at that hour, in unconscious sleep, Jane; perhaps your soul wandered from its cell to comfort mine, for those were your accents—as certain as I live—they were yours!"

Reader, it was on Monday night—near midnight—that I too had received the mysterious summons; those were the very words by which I replied to it. I listened to Mr. Rochester's narrative, but made no disclosure in return. The coincidence struck me as too awful and inexplicable to be communicated or discussed. If I told anything, my tale would be such as must necessarily make a profound impression on the mind of my hearer; and that mind, yet from its sufferings too prone to gloom, needed not the deeper shade of the supernatural. I kept these things then, and pondered them in my heart.

"You cannot now wonder," continued my master, "that when you rose upon me so unexpectedly last night, I had difficulty believing you any other than a mere voice and vision: something that would melt to silence as the midnight whisper had melted before. Now, I thank God! I know it to be otherwise. Yes, I thank God!"

He put me off his knee, rose, and bending his sightless eyes to the earth, he stood in mute devotion. Only the last words of his worship were audible. "I thank my Maker that in the midst of judgment He has remembered mercy. I humbly entreat my Redeemer to give me strength to lead henceforth a purer life than I have done hitherto!"

Then he stretched out his hand to be led. I took that dear hand, held it to my lips, then let it pass round my shoulder; and we entered the wood, and wended homeward.

CHAPTER XX

READER, I MARRIED HIM. A QUIET WEDDING we had; he and I, the parson and clerk, were alone present. When we got back from church, I went into the kitchen, where Mary was cooking the dinner, and John cleaning the knives, and I said:

"Mary, I have been married to Mr. Rochester this morning."

The housekeeper and her husband were both of that decent phlegmatic order of people to whom one may safely communicate a piece of news without having one's ears pierced by shrill ejaculation. Mary did stare, and the ladle, with which she was basting a pair of chickens roasting at the fire, did for some three minutes hang suspended in the air, and John's knives also had a rest from the polishing process; then John grinned, and Mary said only:

"Have you, Miss? Well, for sure!"

I wrote to Moor House immediately, to say what I had done; Diana and Mary approved the step unreservedly. How St. John received the news, I don't know; he never answered the letter in which I communicated it; yet six months after, he wrote to me without, however, alluding to my marriage. His letter was then calm and kind, and he has maintained a regular, though not frequent correspondence, ever since.

I have now been married ten years. I know what it is to live entirely for and with what I love best on earth. I hold myself supremely blest—blest beyond what language can express. I know no weariness of my Edward's society; he knows none of mine. To be together is for us to be at once as free as in solitude, as gay as in company.

Mr. Rochester continued blind for the first two years of our union; perhaps it was that circumstance that drew us so very near—that knit us so very close, for I was then his vision, as I am still his right hand. He saw nature—he saw books through me; and never did I weary of gazing for his behalf, and of putting into words the effect of field, tree, town, river, cloud, sunbeam—of the landscape before us; of the weather round us—and impressing by sound on his ear what light could no longer stamp on his eye.

Then one morning at the end of the two years, as I was writing a letter to his dictation, he came and bent over me, and said:

"Jane, have you a glittering ornament round your neck?"

I had a gold watch chain. I answered, "Yes."

"And have you a pale blue dress on?"

I had. He informed me then that for some time he had fancied the obscurity clouding one eye was becoming less dense, and that now he was sure of it. He went then to an eminent oculist; and he eventually recovered the sight of that one eye. He cannot now see very distinctly, or read much; but he can find his way without being led by the hand; the sky is no longer a blank to him—the earth no longer a void. When his firstborn was put into his arms, he could see that the boy had inherited his own eyes, as they once were—large, brilliant and black. On that occasion, he again, with a full heart, acknowledged that God had tempered justice with mercy.

My Edward and I, then, are happy, and the more so, because those we most love are happy likewise. Little Adèle is now grown quite a young lady, and is docile, good-tempered and well-principled. Diana and Mary Rivers are both married; alternately, once every year, they come to see us, and we go to see them. Diana's husband is a captain in the navy; Mary's is a clergyman. Both Captain Fitzjames and Mr. Wharton love their wives, and are loved by them.

As to St. John Rivers, he left England; he went to India. He entered on the path he had marked for himself; he pursues it still. Firm, faithful and devoted; full of energy and zeal, and truth, he labors on.

He is unmarried; he will never marry now. Himself has hitherto sufficed to the toil; and the toil draws near its close: his glorious sun hastens to its setting. The last letter I received from him drew tears from my eyes, and yet filled my heart with divine joy: he anticipated his sure reward, his incorruptible crown. And why weep for this? No fear of death will darken St. John's last hour: his hope will be sure, his faith steadfast. His own words are a pledge of this:

"My Master," he says, "has forewarned me. Daily he announces more distinctly, 'Surely I come quickly!' and hourly I more eagerly respond, 'Amen; even so come, Lord Jesus!'"